WORKING OUT

with Listening

Vicki Lord Larson • Angela Sterling-Orth
Sarah A. Thurs

Super Duper® Publication
Greenville, SC

10   09   08   8 7 6 5 4

Library of Congress Cataloging-in-Publication Data
Larson, Vicki Lord.
   Working out with listening / Vicki Lord Larson, Angela Sterling-
Orth,
Sarah A. Thurs.
      p. cm.
Includes bibliographical references.
   ISBN 1-888222-97-2 (pbk.)
   1. Listening—Problems, exercises, etc. I. Sterling-Orth, Angela,
date. II. Thurs, Sarah A., date. III. Title.
   BF323.L5 L37 2002
   372.69'044—dc21

                                         2002073656

Printed in the United States of America
Cover design by Debbie Olson

P. O. Box 24997, Greenville, SC 29616-2497 USA
www.superduper.com
1-800-277-8738 • Fax 1-800-978-7379

Acknowledgments

We would like to thank our field reviewers—Peg Hutson-Nechkash, Kelly Mattison, and Linda Robideau—for using the Workouts with their students. Their insightful feedback and suggestions helped make *Working Out with Listening* a much friendlier resource.

Contents

Introduction

Overview

Working Out with Listening is a resource full of 50 quick, fun, pick-and-choose Workouts that provide practice in the area of listening. This book is perfect for educators and parents who want to provide children with extra listening practice in the areas of recalling information, following directions, and listening for details and main ideas.

The Workouts review or reinforce listening skills that are expected to emerge naturally. They can be used as warm-ups before presenting a more complete lesson, as cool-downs at the end of a lesson, or as quick exercises when a few extra minutes remain between activities at school or at home. The Workouts can also be used informally to probe listening strengths and weaknesses.

Because adults read the items in each Workout and help children judge correct and incorrect responses, children do not need to be readers to complete the Workouts. The skills targeted through the Workouts are appropriate for children between 5 and 10 years of age, but they may also be appropriate for older children who have difficulty with listening tasks.

Each of the 50 Workouts includes 3 exercises focusing on the following areas of listening:

1. Recalling Information
2. Following Directions
3. Listening for Details & Main Ideas

Each Workout also has a Think About Challenge. These 50 tasks tap into related listening skills, such as identifying appropriate and inappropriate listening behaviors, participating in listening role-plays, and listening to draw inferences.

Not all exercises within a Workout need to be completed. An Item Analysis (see pages 25–28) provides a handy breakdown of all 150 exercises (not including the 50 Think About Challenges) so that particular types of exercises can be selected based on the listening skill area they target. For example, 10 short tasks for targeting the skill of Listening for Details could easily be chosen from the 50 Workouts.

Target Users

The exercises in *Working Out with Listening* are intended for use with children in kindergarten to grade 4. They may also be appropriate for older students who are in the 5- to 10-year developmental age range. In addition, the tasks are useful for older children who have difficulty listening, such as those diagnosed with a central auditory processing disorder. The Workouts can be used by elementary school teachers, speech-language pathologists, learning disabilities specialists, reading specialists, special educators, and families.

Goals

The main goal of *Working Out with Listening* is to provide children with practice opportunities for improving their listening skills. In addition, exercises can be selected to informally probe children's strengths and weaknesses in listening. The following skills can be reinforced using the Workouts:

- Recalling strings of 3, 4, and 5 digits in the same or the opposite order

- Recalling strings of 3, 4, and 5 related or unrelated words in the same or the opposite order

2

- Recalling 1- and 2-syllable or 3- and 4-syllable non-sense words

- Recalling simple, compound, complex, and compound-complex sentences

- Recalling yes/no, negative, *wh-,* compound, and tag questions

- Following one-, two-, three-, four- and five-step directions using actions, common objects, and paper-and-pencil tasks

- Following one-, two-, three-, four- and five-step directions using Simon Says tasks

- Recalling requested details from single sentences, short passages, and paragraphs read aloud

- Recognizing and stating the main idea of short paragraphs read aloud

- Extending the main idea of short paragraphs read aloud

In addition, the exercises may be useful for generalizing the use of conversational skills (e.g., listening, turn taking, and topic management) and for practicing articulation and fluency skills in a conversational context.

Listening

Definition

Listening is the reception and use of information that is transmitted acoustically (Nicolosi, Harryman, and Kresheck, 1996). This definition suggests that listening encompasses more than simply hearing a message. Listening is a receptive skill that involves three primary processes: a physical process, an interpretive process, and an analytical process (Mead and

Rubin, 1985). The physical process of listening is the act of hearing what is being said. The interpretive process of listening is the act of understanding the information that is being said. The analytical process of listening is the act of judging the information that is being said and determining whether the information that is heard and understood makes sense (The Learning Network, 2001).

Listening is greatly influenced by factors such as distractions, the listener's motivation, the length of the message, and the integrity of the listener (Nicolosi et al., 1996). Consequently, it is important to provide children with appropriate listening instruction so that they can learn how to be effective, active listeners.

Rationale

Listening is the most primary communication activity. It provides a foundation for acquiring all other aspects of language and cognition (Steil, 1982). Furthermore, literacy and classroom success are directly related to a student's listening knowledge, attitudes, and behaviors (Steil), since children in grades 1 through 5 have been found to spend 57.5% of their classroom activity engaged in listening (Wilt, 1950).

Children who struggle to acquire and use effective listening strategies are at a clear disadvantage during academic and social interactions. These children can miss important messages related to the acquisition of new knowledge, the required expectations for performance, and social interactions or cues. Missing out on these critical messages can lead to classroom failure and strained social relationships. Even worse, speech and language impairments, hyperactivity, depression, and autism can be closely intertwined with underdeveloped listening skills (Madaule, 1994).

A child with strong listening skills is more likely to have better thinking and reasoning skills. What's more, listening skills can increase a child's sense of self-worth as he or she learns how to communicate effectively with others (Klein, 2001).

Development

Listening skills develop from birth and advance throughout a person's life (Steil, 1982). By 3 months of age, infants begin to demonstrate early listening skills when they calm to a familiar voice, recognize their own name, stop performing an action in response to the command "No," and distinguish between angry and friendly voices (Rossetti, 1990). By one year of age, children demonstrate more observable listening skills by following simple commands (e.g., "Wipe your face"), attending to objects that are mentioned, and responding to simple questions (e.g., "Where is Daddy?") (Rossetti). Children demonstrate listening skills by following one-step commands by 15 months of age, two-step commands by 33 months of age, and three-step commands by 36 months of age (Rossetti).

As children begin to participate in true conversations, their listening skills continue to develop. By three years of age, children can typically trade off the listener and speaker role when interacting with one other person for up to two exchanges (Bloom, Rocissano, and Hood, 1976). This number of exchanges continues to grow as a child ages, and a child gains proficiency with the listener role earlier than the speaker role (Kraus and Glucksberg, 1969). By five years of age, children begin to develop the use of some listener responses (e.g., nodding their head to show understanding or saying "Huh?" to show lack of understanding), although the use of such behaviors remains relatively low until adolescence (Dittman, 1972).

Using *Working Out with Listening*

Uses

Working Out with Listening can be used to reinforce and review or to informally assess children's listening skills. Each Workout contains one exercise for each of three types of listening behaviors and one Think About Challenge. Workouts can be used in their entirety or in part, depending on the skill level of the children involved.

Reinforcement and Review

When using a Workout to reinforce listening skills, be sure to consider the relative ease or difficulty of each task. A slight range of difficulty may exist for some Workouts. Overall, however, the Workouts progress from the easiest tasks in Workout #1 to the most difficult tasks in Workout #50. (Refer to the Item Analysis [see pages 25–28] for a detailed breakdown of the types and locations of exercises found in each Workout.) This format allows you to address individual children's needs by picking and choosing developmentally appropriate Workouts.

Informal Assessment

The Workouts are excellent stimuli for gathering data regarding a child's strengths and weaknesses in the area of listening. Since a wide range of tasks are included, they can be used to probe a variety of skills (e.g., attending, following directions, and recognizing main ideas).

Periodically, gather assessment data in a one-to-one situation with a child by presenting one or more appropriate exercises to him or her. Ideally, establish a baseline and measure change at key points—such as quarterly, at year-end, and/or during a review of an individualized education program (IEP). Workouts that include repetition of digit strands and repetition

6

of nonsense words are ideal for use during informal assessment. Repeating digits (forward and backward) and repeating nonsense words truly tap into recall skills since the linguistic content is minimal or absent (Montgomery, 1996). The 20 Workouts that are recommended for informal assessment are marked with a clipboard icon. Use the *Recording Form* in the appendix (see pages 20–21) to indicate the child's correct and incorrect responses for each type of listening skill. The form can be used to collect data on up to 25 children. Duplicate additional copies as needed. Since normative data on these types of skills are lacking or nonexistent, consider collecting data on many children over time and establishing local norms.

When to Use

Working Out with Listening can be used at various times. A Workout can be used as a quick start of a class or session to prepare children for learning. A complete Workout might be appropriate for a group of third graders; whereas, a partial Workout might be all that is needed for a kindergarten group.

A Workout could also be used, in whole or in part, at the end of a lesson. This is especially helpful when a lesson has ended and there is insufficient time remaining to start a new lesson.

Consider using a Workout as a fun filler activity when a group of children are waiting for an event (e.g., before lunch, on bus rides, or while waiting for another activity to begin). (Avoid Workouts that have a drawing component or that require the use of manipulatives when conducting the activity out of the typical classroom setting.) The Workouts could also be offered as an option during "free time" or indoor recess, as long as an adult is available to read the exercises

to the children. For even more ideas for using *Working Out with Listening,* refer to "Additional Suggestions," beginning on page 14.

Presenting the Exercises

As mentioned previously, each Workout includes three types of exercises. When presenting an exercise, read each item aloud. Be sure to provide explicit instructions for responding to each exercise, especially if an exercise type is new to a child or group of children. For example, when using a Following Directions exercise for the first time, say something like "I will be reading directions for you to follow. You need to listen carefully to everything I say before you start performing the direction. For example, if I say 'Show me your elbow and then show me your knee,' you should listen to both directions first and then do everything that I said in the order that I said it." Provide additional examples whenever necessary. Use techniques to augment directions when appropriate. For example, modify your voice inflection when asking questions or giving a direction to be followed. (See "Additional Suggestions" for more ideas.) Always be certain that the instructions are clear.

Care has been taken to control the vocabulary level of items in each exercise. However, by providing tasks appropriate for kindergartners through fourth graders, vocabulary may be too difficult for younger children or too easy for older children. When this occurs, substitute appropriate vocabulary or choose a different exercise. For the most part, the Workouts progress in order from the easiest to the most difficult. Care was taken to attempt to make the difficulty level of each task within a single Workout somewhat consistent.

The answers to the exercises should be obvious to educators. Some items require only one-word responses while others are open ended. For example, when asked to answer a question by extending information presented in a short paragraph, children have numerous correct ways to complete the task. Multiple possibilities for answers encourages flexible thinking and promotes metacognitive development.

Exercise Directions

There are three exercises and one Think About Challenge per Workout. The following is a description of each type of exercise with specific instructions when helpful.

1. *Recalling Information:* The recall tasks are presented using a variety of stimuli: digits, related words, unrelated words, nonsense words, sentences, and questions. Children practice their listening and recall skills as they repeat a string of numbers or words in the same or the opposite order as the facilitator (e.g., "Listen to each set of related words. Then repeat the words in the same order that you hear them: *cloud, sky, stars, moon"),* repeat nonsense words (e.g., *bowlidma),* or repeat increasingly complex questions or sentences after the facilitator (e.g., "Have you been waiting in line or did you just get here?").

   Orient children to the expectations of a recall task so that listening, rather than orientation or memory skills are being targeted. For example, prepare students by letting them know that they'll be hearing a string of digits or words and that they are to listen carefully so that they are able to repeat what is heard. Many of the recall tasks, such as repeating of nonsense words or strings of digits, inherently reduce the challenge of linguistic comprehension due to their nature. This makes these tasks excellent for exercising children's basic

listening skills. Talk with children about how all of the recall tasks are great listening exercises.

2. *Following Directions:* These tasks require students to listen to and perform one-, two-, three-, four-, and five-step directives. Movement tasks and drawing activities are used throughout the 50 Workouts. At times, Simon Says tasks are also used. These tasks require that students not only listen to the directive, but also pay attention to whether "Simon" actually said that the directive should be completed.

For each task, the order of the actions is imperative. Be sure to remind students to listen to an entire string of directions before performing the actions in the order they are stated. If needed, for younger children or for those who struggle with memory demands, have students perform the directives as you pause between each individual statement. Work toward having the children be successful waiting for an entire direction to be spoken before they begin their response.

For some of the Following Directions tasks, children's responses may vary, but still be accurate. For example, when told to "Show me a short finger," some students may hold up their pinky finger, while others may indicate their thumb. Or, when told to "Put your hand near your ear," students may choose slightly different distances. This variety of responses is acceptable, and children should learn that slightly different responses can still be deemed appropriate.

From time to time, a materials icon appears alongside a Following Directions task. These

10

tasks require the use of the following items: 9 pennies, a pencil, and a blank sheet of paper. Gather one set of materials for each child participating in the Workout, or have children take turns using one set of materials and alternating the role of listener for the Workouts that require the use of these materials. Encourage children to keep their eyes on their own materials during these activities. Watch the children as they follow these directions. As needed, after a set of directions has been read and completed, have children compare their materials to one another and/or to the educator's model.

Drawing Activity At other times, a paper-and-pencil icon will appear alongside a task. These activities require that each child have two blank sheets of paper and a pencil. Have students use the backs of the papers as needed. Children should be encouraged to keep their eyes on their own papers during these activities. After a set of directions has been read and drawn, have children compare their papers to one another and/or to the educator's model.

3. *Listening for Details & Main Ideas:* These tasks are broken down into two types: those requiring identification of specific details in sentences read aloud and those asking for a statement related to the main idea of passages read aloud. Identifying the main idea requires the understanding and synthesis all the details presented in a passage. Thus, the tasks requiring identification of a single detail are considered simpler and are presented in the earlier Workouts. Tasks for listening for details include short, medium, and long passages. The length reflects the number of words and the amount of detail in a passage, which contributes to the difficulty level of

each. Listening for main ideas tasks include those that require children to answer by simply stating the main idea and those that require children to recognize the main idea, but answer a related question that extends the main idea. The extension tasks are considered more difficult and are presented in the later Workouts.

Prepare children for these tasks by giving them listening guidance such as "Pay close attention to this story" or "Think about what this story is about as I am reading." Consider injecting other verbal support if children struggle with these tasks. For example, saying, "My main point is..." before stating the main idea, restating the main ideas at the end of the passage, or repeating specific details can increase children's chances of paying attention to important information. Reduce this support as possible.

4. *Think About Challenge:* Each Workout contains a Think About Challenge designed to tap into higher level listening skills. The tasks are considered challenging because they encourage flexible thinking and are meant to extend children's application of listening knowledge. Appropriate and inappropriate listening behaviors, roleplays relating to listening skills, and inferential tasks are incorporated into the 50 Think About Challenges.

Mediation of the Exercises

As structured, the Workouts provide an abundance of practice to improve listening skills. Adults using this resource should be aware that children may fail to apply the skills used in the Workout exercises to other relevant activities unless mediation accompanies the exercises.

When an adult mediates for a child, he or she focuses the child's attention on the salient characteristics of the task with the intention to go beyond the task at hand. The concern is not just to have the child respond to the listening exercises, but to understand the skills and strategies needed to perform the listening task and to recognize other academic, social, or vocational situations in which those skills and strategies are required.

A prime way to focus a child's attention is to present questions such as the following:

- "Are you finding it easy or difficult to be a careful listener during these exercises? Why?"

- "Now that we've done a few items, let's stop and think about what you're doing that helps you listen carefully. What do you do in your mind to pay attention and figure out the answers?"

- "It seems like you're having some trouble with the exercise. Let's talk about what might be making it hard for you to listen right now." (Discuss possible distractions.) "Let's talk about what you could do now and during other situations to deal with these types of distractions."

- "When have you (name the skill: repeated a set of numbers, followed a set of directions, listened to understand the main idea) at school? At home? With your friends?"

Younger children will almost always need help verbalizing their responses. Be prepared to model a response using language at the child's level. Even older children frequently need help formulating their responses since often they can do the tasks but they cannot explain what they were thinking about or what makes certain activities challenging for them. Without

assistance from an adult mediator, children may also fail to see how listening skills can help them in other places in the school or in community and home settings.

Certainly, you can use the exercises in this book in a straightforward manner without ever discussing them. However, *mediated learning theory* (Feuerstein, 1980) suggests that combining mediation with the exercises facilitates generalization of the skills. This helps the child be more receptive to learning about the same skills (in this case, listening skills) in other situations. It also helps children connect what they have learned to related skills; therefore, they become independent learners.

Additional Suggestions

1. Be sure to have children's attention before beginning each task. Use a child's name or adopt a visual and/or auditory cue that means it is time to be active listeners (e.g., turning the lights in the room off and then on again). It is crucial that everyone participating knows that it is time to listen, that listening skills can be practiced and improved, and that the listening skills that are practiced during a Workout should also be used during other classroom and social situations.

2. As children take turns responding to items in the exercises, involve the children waiting for their turn in active listening. The following are examples of ways to include all children in a task when only one child is being asked to complete the task:

   a. Have children give a thumbs-up or thumbs-down signal to indicate if the responding child accurately completes an item.

b. Randomly call on a child to listen to and repeat the responding child's answer, if the answer is appropriate. This opportunity may improve motivation to listen during other students' turns.

3. Help children understand the appropriate use of eye contact for different listening situations. Model and encourage the use of eye contact by saying things like "This direction has some actions involved. Watch and listen to me as I read the direction," "Did you notice how Ethan watched Jeffrey during that role play? That was great use of eye contact," and "Did it help to watch me while I read the directions?"

   Help children see that appropriate use of eye contact does not mean they must keep their eyes on the speaker at all times. Instead, help them understand that looking directly at the speaker is essential at times, but does not always contribute to effective listening skills (e.g., when listening for the main idea of a passage that is read, sometimes a student might process the information better if he or she is not watching the speaker). Also discuss how eye contact is not needed when listening during certain situations (e.g., when talking on the telephone, when listening to an audio program).

4. Model and encourage children to use specific social skills related to listening behavior. For example, have children practice using facial expressions that show they are listening to the speaker. Encourage children to use a puzzled look when they do not understand what is being said. Explain how these subtle cues can help prevent and repair communication breakdowns

that sometimes occur during tasks that rely heavily on listening skills.

5. Encourage children to ask questions and make statements to clarify information as needed. Reassure them that even careful listeners miss information at times and that asking questions or restating what was heard is often the best way to repair a communication interaction and demonstrate active listening. Offer praise to children when they ask relevant questions in order to clarify information. Suggest that they ask a question when they seem confused about what was heard. Say things such as "Great question. I will repeat the list of words again. Listen carefully," "Is there a question you could ask to clarify that information?", and "Maybe you could ask me to repeat the direction again if you're having trouble remembering what I said."

6. Encourage children to become aware of potential distractions and help them recognize things that are particularly distracting to them. Show children how to minimize distractions during the listening activities. Assist them as they attempt to make the environment less distracting for themselves. For example, allow children to move to a seat that is closer to the speaker, agree to close the door or windows if distractions are happening outside of the room, and request other children to stop talking as tasks are being read.

7. Use the Workouts as the basis for a competitive game between two teams. Award points or chips to teams for correct answers. Use the Think About Challenge exercises to break ties or to award bonus points. Be creative in how you set up the game rules, or involve

children in deciding how to structure the game. Designing a competition and encouraging children to work as a team can increase their motivation to be better listeners.

8. When a child is struggling to respond to an item, provide as much scaffolding and cuing as needed to help him or her succeed in the task. The following are examples:

   a. Shorten sentences or repeat text containing important information. For example, for a task in which children are to recall a string of five digits, shorten each item so that only three digits are presented.

   b. Provide visuals to aid the child's performance. Locate actual objects or pictures of items presented in an exercise. For example, show a carton of juice when reading the passage in Workout #31 for Listening for Details & Main Ideas. As children listen to you talk about the healthful benefits of juice, the visual aid may increase their active listening skills and facilitate comprehension.

   c. Have the child repeat items following the adult presentation. For example, when having a child perform the task "First stand up, then turn around, and last clap your hands," encourage him or her to repeat the direction before performing it.

   d. Provide multiple choices for the child. For example, if an item directs a child to listen and answer the following question "Amy and James went to the store. Who went to the store?" you could instead ask "Did Seth and Karen go to the store or did Amy and James go to the store?"

17

e. Turn a task into a cloze procedure, providing the first part of a desired response and prompting the child to complete the response. For example, instead of asking the child to listen and state the main idea of a passage, read the passage and then say, "The story I just read told about how important it is to...."

f. Encourage older children to take notes while listening, especially during the Listening for Details & Main Ideas tasks. Model effective note-taking skills by showing students how to write down key words and phrases rather than transcribing verbatim. That way, listening skills are still targeted and study skills are incorporated. Draw children's attention to how note-taking can be a powerful tool.

g. Foreshadow information children should be listening for. For example, say, "When I'm finished reading this paragraph, I will be asking you to tell me the name of the person who is receiving the special award."

h. Remove sequential cues to make tasks more challenging. For example, for the three- through five-step Following Directions exercises, the words *first, then,* and *last* could be removed from each direction. Be certain that children understand that they must still preform each task in the order stated.

9. Define or explain unfamiliar vocabulary that might be included in a task. For example, if a child is asked to show you the emotion ecstatic, be sure he or she is clear about what that word means so that you are practicing listening (and not semantic) skills.

10. Make tasks more challenging by asking follow-up questions. For example, after a child correctly identifies the main idea of a passage that is read, ask an inference question related to the passage to challenge the child with the skill of inferring additional information from what is known. Or, after a single content question is asked, follow up with additional content questions.

11. Extend tasks to tap into metalinguistic skills by asking children to explain their responses. For example, if a child is asked to recall a string of 4 unrelated words, also request that he or she explain the listening and memory strategy he or she used to recall all 4 words.

12. Add increased challenge to tasks by having children generate written responses. Then have them exchange papers and check each other's answers, if appropriate. This may work especially well for the Recalling Information tasks. Since the purpose of these tasks is for children to practice their listening skills, continue to read these tasks aloud when presenting the Workout. However, to promote writing practice, children could list their individual responses on a piece of paper or on a chalkboard as they generate them.

13. Pay attention to your vocal quality and variety as you present Workouts to the children. Using an energetic and exciting voice may encourage increased listening skills (Madaule, 1994). Using a monotone or harsh voice can deter children from listening attentively. Talk with children about how a speaker's voice can be a distraction and strategize how to overcome such a distraction (e.g., encouraging children to politely request that a speaker increase his or her volume).

Appendix

WORKING OUT
with Listening

Recording Form

Listening Skill Areas

Names	1. Recalling Information	2. Following Directions	3. Listening for Details & Main Ideas	Comments

Names

References

Bloom, L., Rocissano, L, and Hood, L. (1976). Adult-child discourse: Developmental interaction between information processing and linguistic interaction. *Cognitive Psychology, 8*(4), 521–552.

Dittman, A. (1972). Developmental factors in conversational behavior. *Journal of Communication, 22*(4), 404–423.

Feuerstein, R. (1980). *Instrumental enrichment.* Chicago: Scott Foresman.

Klein, K. (2001). *Parent connection: Learning to listen.* Retrieved October 5, 2001, from Pre-K Smarties website: www.preksmarties.com/connection

Kraus, R., and Glucksberg. S. (1969). The development of communication: Competence as a function of age. *Child Development, 40*(1), 255–266.

The Learning Network. (2001). *Homework center: Speaking and listening skills.* Retrieved October 5, 2001, from www.factmonster.com/homework/listeningskills1.html

Madaule, P. (1994). *When listening comes alive: A guide to effective learning and communication.* Norval, Ontario: Moulin.

Mead, N.A., and Rubin, D.L. (1985). *Assessing listening and speaking skills.* Urbana, IL: ERIC Clearinghouse on Reading and Communication Skills. (ERIC Document Reproduction Service No. ED263626)

Montgomery, J. (1996). Sentence comprehension and working memory in children with specific language impairment. *Topics in Langauge Disorders, 17*(1), 19–32.

Nicolosi, L., Harryman, E., and Kresheck, J. (1996). *Terminology of communication disorders: Speech-language-hearing* (4th ed.). Baltimore: Williams and Wilkins.

Rossetti, L. (1990). *The Rossetti infant-toddler language scale: A measure of communication and interaction.* East Moline, IL: LinguiSystems.

Steil, L.K. (1982). The secondary teacher's listening resource unit. St. Paul, MN: Communication Development.

Wilt, M.E. (1950). A study of teacher awareness of listening as a factor in elementary education. *Journal of Educational Research, 43,* 626–636.

Item Analysis

Recalling Information

Digits

Listen to each set of numbers. Then repeat the numbers in the same order that you hear them.	1, 2, 5, 6, 11
Listen to each set of numbers. Then repeat the numbers in the opposite order that you hear them.	16, 17, 18, 19, 24

Related Words

Listen to each set of related words. Then repeat the words in the same order that you hear them.	3, 7, 8, 12, 13
Listen to each set of related words. Then repeat the words in the opposite order that you hear them.	20, 21, 25, 26, 29

Unrelated Words

Listen to each set of unrelated words. Then repeat the words in the same order that you hear them.	4, 9, 10, 14, 15
Listen to each set of unrelated words. Then repeat the words in the opposite order that you hear them.	22, 23, 27, 28, 30

WORKING OUT
with Listening

Exercise Type	Workout Number

Nonsense Words (1- & 2-Syllable)

Listen to each nonsense word. Then repeat it.	31, 32, 33, 34, 35

Nonsense Words (3- & 4-Syllable)

Listen to each nonsense word. Then repeat it.	36, 37, 38, 39, 40

Sentences & Questions

Listen to each sentence. Then repeat it.	41, 42, 43, 44, 49
Listen to each question. Then repeat it.	45, 46, 47, 48, 50

Following Directions

One-Step Directions

Listen carefully. Then follow each direction.	1, 3, 4, 6
Simon says...	2, 5, 7

Two-Step Directions

Listen carefully. Then follow both directions.	8, 10, 11, 13, 14
Simon says...	9, 12

Exercise Type	Workout Number
Three-Step Directions	
Listen carefully. Then follow the directions.	15, 17, 19, 20, 21, 23, 24, 26, 27, 28, 29, 31, 33
Simon says...	16, 22, 25, 30
Listen carefully. Then follow the directions. (showing emotions)	18, 32
Four- & Five-Step Directions	
Listen carefully. Then follow the directions.	34, 35, 36, 37, 38, 40, 41, 42, 46, 47, 49, 50
Simon says...	43, 44, 48
Listen carefully. Then follow the directions. (showing emotions)	39, 45

Listening for Details & Main Ideas

Listening for Details

Short tasks	1, 2, 3, 4, 5, 6, 7, 8, 9, 10
Medium tasks	11, 12, 13, 14, 15, 16, 17, 18, 19, 20

Exercise Type	Workout Number
Long tasks	21, 22, 23, 24, 25, 26, 27, 28, 29, 30

Listening for Main Ideas

Stating the main idea	31, 32, 33, 34, 35, 36, 37, 38, 39, 40
Extending the main idea (drawing inferences)	41, 42, 43, 44, 45, 46, 47, 48, 49, 50

Workouts

Listening

Workout #1

Recalling Information

Listen to each set of numbers. Then repeat the numbers in the same order that you hear them.

    1, 3, 4   6, 9, 7

    5, 9, 2   3, 5, 0

    8, 3, 7   9, 4, 8

Following Directions

Listen carefully. Then follow each direction.

    Show me your fingers.

    Point to your head.

    Show me your elbow.

    Show me your knee.

    Point to your nose.

Listening for Details & Main Ideas

Listen carefully. Then answer each question.

Amy and James went to the store. Who went to the store?

A bear and a deer were in the road. What was in the road?

The candy bar cost 50 cents. How much did the candy bar cost?

Maria's favorite color is pink. Whose favorite color is pink?

She named the cat Snowball because it was white. What did she name the cat?

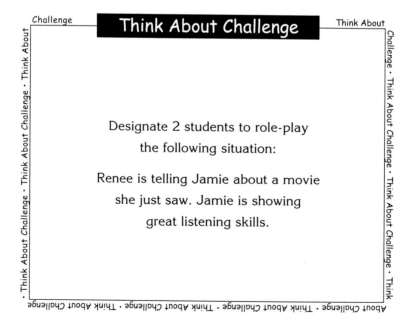

Think About Challenge

Designate 2 students to role-play the following situation:

Renee is telling Jamie about a movie she just saw. Jamie is showing great listening skills.

Listening

Recalling Information

Listen to each set of numbers. Then repeat the numbers in the same order that you hear them.

98, 57, 10	56, 33, 17
21, 89, 16	64, 58, 20
43, 19, 34	33, 11, 72

Following Directions

Listen carefully. Then follow each direction only if Simon says.

Simon says, "Clap your hands."

Walk to the door.

Simon says, "Point to your foot."

Simon says, "Raise your arm."

Touch your ears.

Listening for Details & Main Ideas

Listen carefully. Then answer each question.

The boys met at the movie theatre. Where did the boys meet?

Math class was cancelled today. Which class was cancelled?

Meg and Philip walked home from school. Who walked home from school?

The cup broke in the dishwasher. What broke in the dishwasher?

The children found candy in their desks. What did the children find in their desks?

Think About Challenge

It's hard to be a good listener when two people are talking at the same time. Name 2 other times when it might be hard to be a good listener.

Listening

Recalling Information

Listen to each set of related words. Then repeat the words in the same order that you hear them.

triangle, square, circle   *man, woman, child*

cut, bandage, heal   *letter, word, sentence*

dirt, water, mud   *happy, happier, happiest*

Following Directions

Listen carefully. Then follow each direction.

Put your hand on the floor.

Put your hand in front of your face.

Show me all of your fingers.

Show me the bottom of your foot.

Put your hand under your elbow.

34

Listening for Details & Main Ideas

Listen carefully. Then answer each question.

The bus was late because it ran out of gas. Why was the bus late?

The puppies were named Max and Bo. What were the puppies named?

All the snow melted on Sunday. What day did the snow melt?

I found a wallet under a bench in the park. Where did I find a wallet?

The girl was wearing glasses, but the boy had braces. Who had braces?

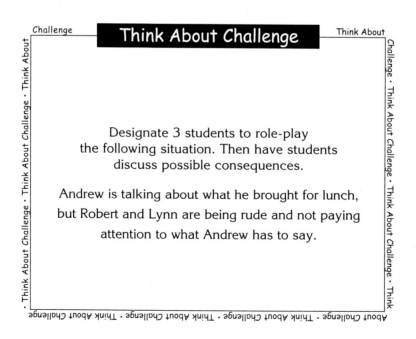

Think About Challenge

Designate 3 students to role-play
the following situation. Then have students
discuss possible consequences.

Andrew is talking about what he brought for lunch,
but Robert and Lynn are being rude and not paying
attention to what Andrew has to say.

Listening

Recalling Information

Listen to each set of unrelated words. Then repeat the words in the same order that you hear them.

ring, turtle, blueberry *backpack, leaf, nice*

button, toenail, building *boat, seven, me*

love, keyboard, ocean *soft, surprised, Friday*

Following Directions

Listen carefully. Then follow each direction.

Put your hand in back of your head.

Put your hand beside your head.

Show me a short finger.

Put your foot on your knee.

Show me the bottom of your shoe.

Listening for Details & Main Ideas

Listen carefully. Then answer each question.

We saw three giraffes and two zebras at the zoo. How many giraffes did we see?

The soda was a dollar and the cookie was 25 cents. How much was the cookie?

His pencil broke, so Ty couldn't finish his work. Why couldn't Ty finish his work?

Peter wanted a ham sandwich and Ellie wanted cheese. Who wanted a ham sandwich?

It rained in the morning and snowed in the afternoon. When did it rain?

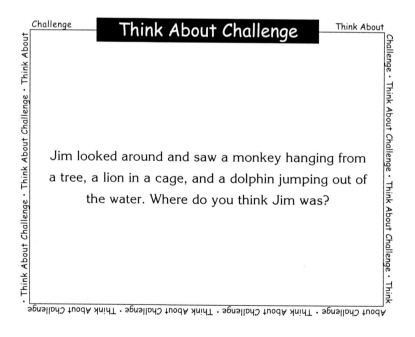

Think About Challenge

Jim looked around and saw a monkey hanging from a tree, a lion in a cage, and a dolphin jumping out of the water. Where do you think Jim was?

 # Listening

Recalling Information

Listen to each set of numbers. Then repeat the numbers in the same order that you hear them.

7, 1, 5, 2	8, 9, 0, 3
0, 6, 7, 1	5, 8, 1, 4
2, 4, 5, 9	7, 6, 2, 3

Following Directions

Listen carefully. Then follow each direction only if Simon says.

Show me your knuckles.

Simon says, "Point to your shoulder."

Put your hand near your ear.

Simon says, "Put your hand far from your eye."

Simon says, "Put your foot in your hand."

Listening for Details & Main Ideas

Listen carefully. Then answer each question.

Greg stayed home because he twisted his ankle. Why did Greg stay home?

The cousins played at the water park all day. Where did the cousins play?

The furniture is on sale for 50% off. What is on sale for 50% off?

The girls will always meet for scouts on Thursdays. Which day will the girls meet for scouts?

Louis forgot his backpack at home. Who forgot his backpack at home?

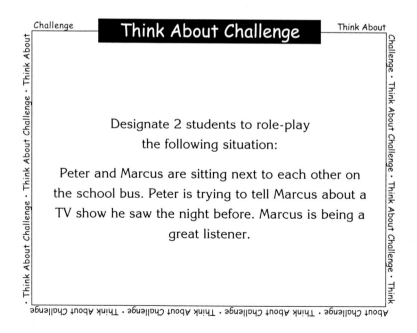

Think About Challenge

Designate 2 students to role-play the following situation:

Peter and Marcus are sitting next to each other on the school bus. Peter is trying to tell Marcus about a TV show he saw the night before. Marcus is being a great listener.

Listening

Recalling Information

Listen to each set of numbers. Then repeat the numbers in the
same order that you hear them.

38, 22, 17, 96	54, 11, 80, 42
64, 39, 15, 31	94, 23, 49, 77
85, 16, 22, 37	54, 68, 21, 81

Following Directions

Listen carefully. Then follow each direction.

With your arms, show me a long line.

With your hands, show me a small circle.

Put your hand next to your head.

With your arms, show me a short line.

With your arms, show me a large circle.

Listening for Details & Main Ideas

Listen carefully. Then answer each question.

Everyone was happy because we had pizza for lunch. Who was happy?

There were five fish in the tank, but only one was red. How many red fish were in the tank?

The kids were allowed to watch 60 minutes of TV per day. How much TV could the kids watch each day?

We went to the mall and then to the movie. Where did we go first?

The mail will be here at 2:00. When will the mail be here?

Think About Challenge

Tell why it is important to be a good listener when someone is giving you directions.

Listening

Recalling Information

Listen to each set of related words. Then repeat the words in the same order that you hear them.

apple, kiwi, grape, pear

rain, snow, hail, sleet

sad, happy, grumpy, mad

dinner, breakfast, lunch, snack

nurse, doctor, hospital, sick

Following Directions

Listen carefully. Then follow each direction only if Simon says.

Simon says, "Show me a few fingers."

With your fingers, show me a wide space.

Simon says, "Point to the bottom of your foot."

Simon says, "Show me the back of your hand."

Simon says, "With your fingers, show me a narrow space."

Listening for Details & Main Ideas

Listen carefully. Then answer each question.

Brian got two shots in his leg. Where did Brian get his shots?

Water, lemons, and ice are needed to make lemonade. What is needed to make lemonade?

Tina and Will live next door to each other. Who lives next door to Will?

Recess is 15 minutes in the morning and 20 minutes in the afternoon. When is the 15-minute recess?

We read 100 books, so we earned a pizza party. How many books did we read?

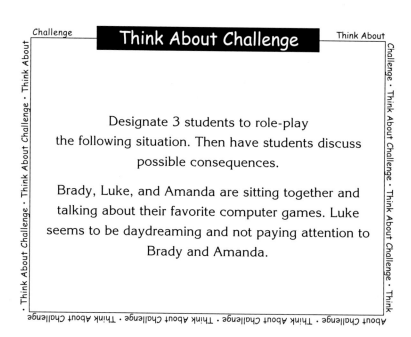

Think About Challenge

Designate 3 students to role-play
the following situation. Then have students discuss
possible consequences.

Brady, Luke, and Amanda are sitting together and
talking about their favorite computer games. Luke
seems to be daydreaming and not paying attention to
Brady and Amanda.

Listening

Recalling Information

Listen to each set of related words. Then repeat the words in the same order that you hear them.

quack, meow, ribbit, peep

over, under, through, around

cloud, sky, stars, moon

snap, buckle, zipper, button

knife, fork, spoon, napkin

Following Directions

Listen carefully. Then follow both directions.

First show me your elbow and then show me your knee.

First put your hand on your knee and then raise your hand.

First point to your eye and then put your hand on your head.

First put your hand on your elbow and then raise your arm.

First point to your shoe and then pat your head.

Listening for Details & Main Ideas

Listen carefully. Then answer each question.

Sam rode his bike to school and Trevor walked. Who rode his bike to school?

Babies and pets were not allowed in the pool. Where were babies and pets not allowed?

Three puppies and two kittens were at the pet store. How many kittens were at the pet store?

Lisa's mom said she'd be home on Tuesday. When will Lisa's mom be home?

There were oatmeal cookies in the cookie jar. What kind of cookies were in the jar?

Think About Challenge

Mary walked into the store and picked up milk, a dozen eggs, bread, and some meat to make hamburgers. What kind of store do you think Mary was in?

Listening

Recalling Information

Listen to each set of unrelated words. Then repeat the words in the same order that you hear them.

cry, best, red, nail

play, old, toy, early

light, pen, drink, sun

chicken, summer, belt, now

sharp, leg, box, high

Following Directions

Listen carefully. Then follow both directions only if Simon says.

Simon says, "First touch the top of your head and then touch your toes."

Simon says, "First touch your nose and then put your hand on your elbow."

First clap your hands and then touch your ears.

Simon says, "First stand up and then turn around twice."

First raise your hand and then touch your nose.

Listening for Details & Main Ideas

Listen carefully. Then answer each question.

The jar had 33 jellybeans and only 3 of them were red. How many jellybeans were in the jar?

Chen borrowed paper from Tim because he left his at home. What did Chen borrow from Tim?

We ordered a pepperoni pizza, but they gave us sausage. What kind of pizza did we order?

Jeri's parents dropped her off at the bowling alley by mistake. Where did Jeri get dropped off?

Colin and Evan were born on the same day. Who were born on the same day?

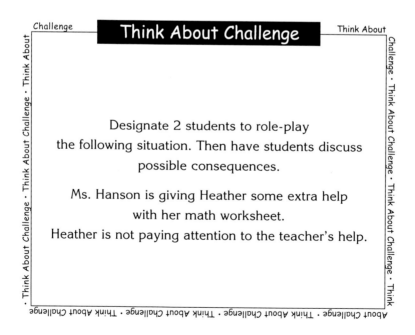

Think About Challenge

Designate 2 students to role-play
the following situation. Then have students discuss
possible consequences.

Ms. Hanson is giving Heather some extra help
with her math worksheet.
Heather is not paying attention to the teacher's help.

Listening

Recalling Information

Listen to each set of unrelated words. Then repeat the words in the same order that you hear them.

tired, flower, tall, plane

elbow, bottom, wish, sleeve

sky, long, first, pear

exercise, thumb, cool, make

black, ladder, inside, giant

Following Directions

Listen carefully. Then follow both directions.

First put your hand in front of your stomach and then put your hand in back of your leg.

First use your fingers to show me wide and then show me narrow.

First put your hand on top of your head and then put your hand under your elbow.

First point to your eyes and then show me your foot.

First use your hands to show me long and then show me short.

Listening for Details & Main Ideas

Listen carefully. Then answer each question.

Carter arrived at 9:00, one hour late. When did Carter arrive?

The babysitter couldn't find the baby's bottle. What couldn't the babysitter find?

Mrs. Anderson will be the soccer coach next season. Who will be the soccer coach?

Yesterday we painted and worked with clay. When did we paint?

We practice our listening skills every day. When do we practice our listening skills?

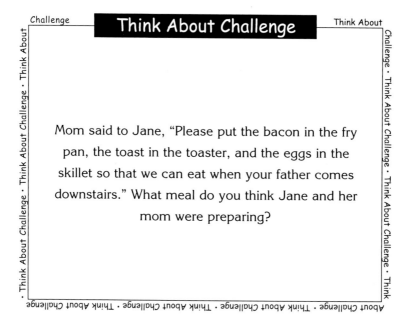

Think About Challenge

Mom said to Jane, "Please put the bacon in the fry pan, the toast in the toaster, and the eggs in the skillet so that we can eat when your father comes downstairs." What meal do you think Jane and her mom were preparing?

Listening

Workout #11

Recalling Information

Listen to each set of numbers. Then repeat the numbers in the
same order that you hear them.

7, 5, 3, 9, 6	0, 4, 2, 3, 6
9, 4, 1, 7, 2	4, 8, 1, 9, 5
1, 3, 2, 5, 9	3, 2, 6, 8, 4

Following Directions

Listen carefully. Then follow both directions.

First use your hands to show me a small circle and then
show me a large circle.

First put your hand beside your head and then put your
hand in front of your face.

First put your hand on top of your head and then put your
hand in back of your head.

First raise your hand high in the air and then put your hand
low to the ground.

First put your hand under your elbow and then put your
hand under your foot.

Listening for Details & Main Ideas

Listen carefully. Then answer the question.

Three boys and four girls were on the bus when it got stuck in the snow. All the students were late for school. How many boys and how many girls were on the bus when it got stuck in the snow?

Kelly, Grant, and Mike decided to play outside even though it was raining. Who decided to play outside in the rain?

The cats were playing in the barn and the dogs were running in the hay field. All the animals became nervous when it started to storm. Which animals were in the barn?

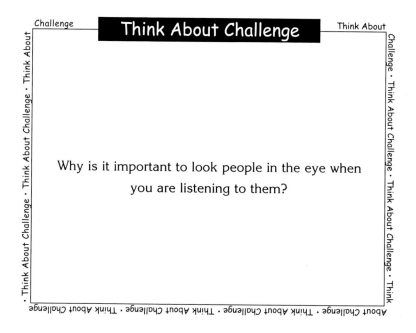

Think About Challenge

Why is it important to look people in the eye when you are listening to them?

Listening

Recalling Information

Listen to each set of related words. Then repeat the words in the same order that you hear them.

pencil, eraser, paper, lines, draw

plant, water, grow, green, dirt

hour, minute, day, week, month

summer, winter, spring, fall, seasons

sleep, dream, snore, night, bed

Following Directions

Listen carefully. Then follow both directions only if Simon says.

Simon says, "First show me your right hand and then point to your left eye."

Simon says, "First put your hand near your ear and then put your hand far away from your head."

First hold up your hand and then show me your first finger.

First show me your last finger and then show me your second finger.

Simon says, "First show me all of your fingers and then show me some of your fingers."

52

Listening for Details & Main Ideas

Listen carefully. Then answer the question.

> We ordered chocolate ice-cream sundaes with extra whipped cream and peanuts. We forgot to ask for cherries on top. What kind of ice cream did we order?

> The teachers and students were eating lunch in the cafeteria when the fire alarm rang. Everyone had to leave the building. Where were the teachers and students when the alarm rang?

> George has piano lessons on Tuesdays and karate class on Thursdays. He also plays on a basketball team on Mondays and Wednesdays. When does George have karate class?

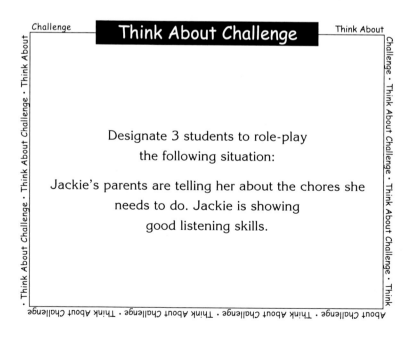

Think About Challenge

Designate 3 students to role-play
the following situation:

Jackie's parents are telling her about the chores she
needs to do. Jackie is showing
good listening skills.

Listening

Workout #13

Recalling Information

Listen to each set of related words. Then repeat the words in the same order that you hear them.

eye, nose, mouth, ear, chin

school, study, learn, books, smart

hug, kiss, love, hold, heart

boots, mittens, hat, earmuffs, scarf

blue, green, yellow, red, pink

Following Directions

Materials Needed!

Listen carefully. Then follow both directions.

First put the pennies in a row and then point to the third penny.

First point to the first penny and then point to the last penny.

First point to the penny in the middle and then give me the second penny.

First put 6 pennies in a circle and then put 2 pennies in the center of the circle.

First give me a few pennies and then put many pennies in a pile.

Listening for Details & Main Ideas

Listen carefully. Then answer the question.

During Sunday's thunderstorm, the power went out and the basement flooded. By Wednesday the power was back on. What day was the thunderstorm?

The new computer is in the first-grade classroom. The second- and third-grade rooms will get new computers next year. Which grade received the new computer?

We went to the store to buy six apples, a dozen eggs, and two loaves of bread. We forgot the eggs, but we also bought cheese. How many apples did we buy?

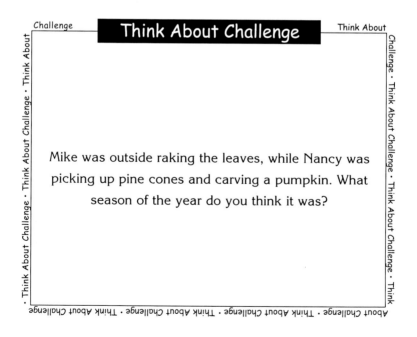

Think About Challenge

Mike was outside raking the leaves, while Nancy was picking up pine cones and carving a pumpkin. What season of the year do you think it was?

Listening

Workout #14

Recalling Information

Listen to each set of unrelated words. Then repeat the words in the same order that you hear them.

flat, eat, in, lake, sing

sticker, purse, sugar, air, pig

pie, ant, math, roll, pick

good, teacher, left, car, all

uncle, window, few, white, at

Following Directions

Drawing Activity

Listen carefully. Then follow both directions.

First draw a large rectangle and then put an *X* in the center of the rectangle.

First draw a circle around the rectangle and then draw an *X* at the top of the page.

First put a circle to the right of the rectangle and then draw a line through the circle.

First put a square on the left side of the rectangle and then draw a line under the square.

First write your name inside the circle on the right and then draw a line through your name.

Listening for Details & Main Ideas

Listen carefully. Then answer the question.

There were three fire engines at the beginning of the parade and two at the end of the parade. The clowns threw candy to the crowd. How many fire engines were in the parade?

Ricky's birthday is in June and mine is in August. I don't know anyone who has a birthday in July. When is Ricky's birthday?

Red roses were growing in Carla's garden and her yard was filled with dandelions. She decided to mow the lawn to get rid of the dandelions. What were growing in Carla's garden?

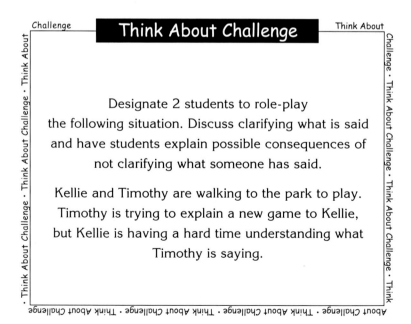

Think About Challenge

Designate 2 students to role-play the following situation. Discuss clarifying what is said and have students explain possible consequences of not clarifying what someone has said.

Kellie and Timothy are walking to the park to play. Timothy is trying to explain a new game to Kellie, but Kellie is having a hard time understanding what Timothy is saying.

Listening

Recalling Information

Listen to each set of unrelated words. Then repeat the words in the same order that you hear them.

oven, do, new, mess, ice

pull, ship, lemon, bat, tip

pole, lose, pine, lip, knee

day, tuna, bush, sail, rest

lamp, drip, lawn, row, TV

Following Directions

Listen carefully. Then follow the directions.

First show me your foot, then point to your ear, and last touch your mouth.

First touch your eye, then point to your nose, and last raise your hand.

First show me your elbow, then point to your shoe, and last touch your arm.

First put your hand on your head, then on your knee, and last on the floor.

First touch your hair, then clap 2 times, and last jump up and down.

, Main Ideas

e question.

lass lines up in the basement
.......~, .~....~ ~ ...~ drill, the class meets on the playground outside. Where does the class go during a tornado drill?

Jon and Jess argued because Jon thought that Jess had stolen his watch. Later, Jon found his watch in his desk and apologized to Jess. Why did Jon and Jess argue?

The dog was wearing a blue collar and the cat was wearing a red collar. Neither animal had tags on its collar. What color was the dog's collar?

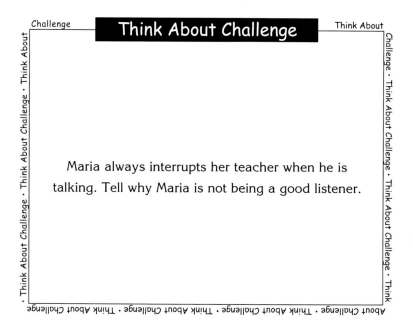

Think About Challenge

Maria always interrupts her teacher when he is talking. Tell why Maria is not being a good listener.

Listening

Workout #16

Recalling Information

Listen to each set of numbers. Then repeat the numbers in the opposite order that you hear them.

2, 0, 5	4, 9, 8
9, 8, 3	7, 6, 0
5, 4, 1	5, 1, 2

Following Directions

Listen carefully. Then follow each direction only if Simon says.

First walk to the door, then sit down, and last touch your nose.

Simon says, "First point to your eye, then touch your arm, and last clap your hands."

Simon says, "First touch your foot, then pat your head, and last point to your ear."

First show me your teeth, then pat your shoulder, and last touch your elbow.

Simon says, "First stand on 1 foot, then clap your hands, and last touch your head."

Listening for Details & Main Ideas

Listen carefully. Then answer the question.

> We made heart-shaped cookies for the party. We decorated the cookies with white frosting and red and pink candy sprinkles. What shape were the cookies?

> The mail carrier was bit by our dog. That same day, the newspaper girl fell on our front steps and hurt her leg. Who was bit by our dog?

> Gina told James that she would meet him in the park at 3:00. When Gina showed up, James was not there. When did Gina say she would meet James in the park?

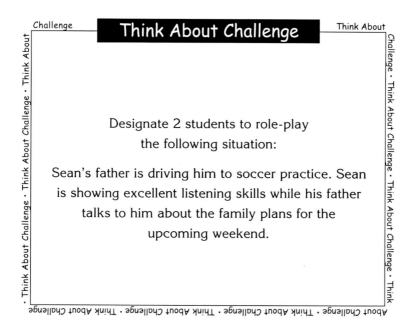

Challenge • Think About Challenge • Think About Challenge • Think About

Think About Challenge

Think About Challenge • Think About Challenge • Think About Challenge • Think

Designate 2 students to role-play the following situation:

Sean's father is driving him to soccer practice. Sean is showing excellent listening skills while his father talks to him about the family plans for the upcoming weekend.

About Challenge • Think About Challenge • Think About Challenge • Think About Challenge

# Listening

Recalling Information

Listen to each set of numbers. Then repeat the numbers in the opposite order that you hear them.

7, 2, 6	5, 2, 9
4, 0, 2	9, 3, 8
3, 1, 4	7, 8, 6

Following Directions

Listen carefully. Then follow the directions.

First put your hand on top of your head, then touch your hand to the floor, and last place your hand on the bottom of your shoe.

First put your hand over your heart, then put your hand on your elbow, and last wave your hand in the air.

First put your arm over your head, then touch your knee, and last put your hand under your chin.

First put your finger near your eye, then put your finger on your foot, and last put your hand in back of your head.

First put your finger under your eye, then point to your eyebrow, and last walk around in a circle.

Listening for Details & Main Ideas

Listen carefully. Then answer the question.

At first I thought I left my coat on the kitchen table. When I couldn't find it anywhere, my whole family helped me look. Finally, we found it in the basement. Where did I first think I left my coat?

Fridays are my favorite day of the week because we have art class and I get to stay up late on Friday nights. Why are Fridays my favorite day of the week?

I found six marbles in my top dresser drawer and a bunch of comic books under my bed when I was cleaning my room. How many marbles did I find?

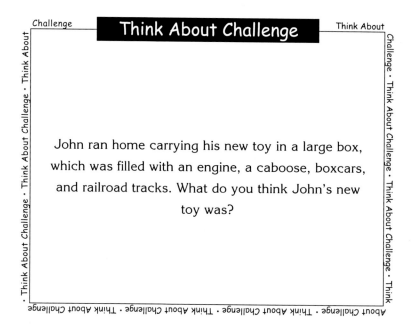

Think About Challenge

John ran home carrying his new toy in a large box, which was filled with an engine, a caboose, boxcars, and railroad tracks. What do you think John's new toy was?

Listening

Recalling Information

Listen to each set of numbers. Then repeat the numbers in the opposite order that you hear them.

54, 13, 65   42, 81, 17

39, 41, 12   74, 62, 91

14, 91, 28   83, 26, 72

Following Directions

Listen carefully. Then follow the directions.

First show me happy, then show me sad, and last show me afraid.

First show me afraid, then show me tired, and last show me bored.

First show me confused, then show me bored, and last show me happy.

First show me excited, then show me crying, and last show me surprised.

First show me sad, then show me angry, and last show me happy.

Listening for Details & Main Ideas

Listen carefully. Then answer the question.

Patty's Pizza Place is my favorite restaurant, but my dad likes Bert's Burger Barn the best. We take turns choosing where to eat. Which restaurant is my favorite?

We served lemonade and water at the summer picnic. Most people liked the lemonade better, but I thought the water was better because it was colder. What did we serve to drink at the picnic?

The nurse and the doctor took turns checking on Chris. The nurse took his temperature and the doctor listened to his heart. What was the patient's name?

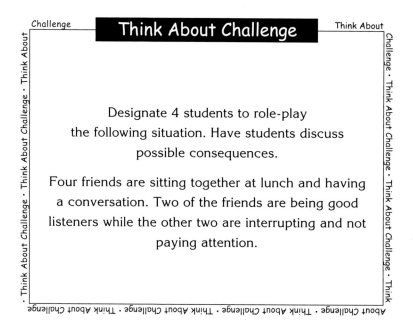

Challenge — **Think About Challenge** — Think About

Designate 4 students to role-play
the following situation. Have students discuss
possible consequences.

Four friends are sitting together at lunch and having
a conversation. Two of the friends are being good
listeners while the other two are interrupting and not
paying attention.

Listening

Recalling Information

Listen to each set of numbers. Then repeat the numbers in the opposite order that you hear them.

38, 41, 52   20, 16, 31

67, 10, 18   56, 87, 34

92, 37, 46   19, 12, 75

Following Directions

Listen carefully. Then follow the directions.

First rub your head, then touch your ear, and last blink your eyes.

First touch your knee, then wave your hands, and last rub your cheek.

First hold up 4 fingers, then raise your other hand, and last touch your eyebrows.

First put your hand in front of your face, then raise your arm, and last clap your hands.

First show me 3 fingers, then touch your eye, and last touch both of your feet.

Listening for Details & Main Ideas

Listen carefully. Then answer the question.

> We visited the farm in June and then we went to the zoo in July. We're still making plans for a trip in August too. In which month did we visit the farm?

> Jake was playing basketball in the driveway when he heard a loud bang come from inside the garage. Where was Jake playing basketball?

> The children had to go to bed early because they were sick with the flu. The next day they felt a lot better, but still stayed home from school. Why did the children go to bed early?

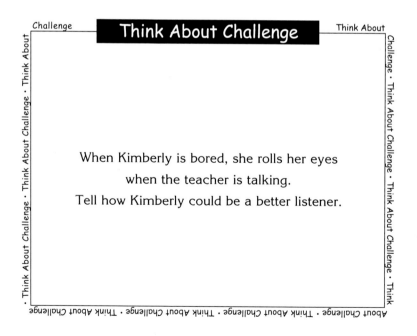

Think About Challenge

When Kimberly is bored, she rolls her eyes when the teacher is talking.
Tell how Kimberly could be a better listener.

Listening

Recalling Information

Listen to each set of related words. Then repeat the words in the opposite order that you hear them.

beginning, middle, end   *sweet, sour, bitter*

heat, fire, flicker   *warm, cold, hot*

child, baby, teenager   *Tuesday, Wednesday, Friday*

Following Directions

Listen carefully. Then follow the directions.

First touch the bottom of your shoe, then touch the top of your head, and last say your name.

First count backward from 5, then count up to 10, and last clap your hands.

First wave your hand, then touch your knee, and last touch your elbow.

First show me your little finger, then rub your eyebrows, and last touch the back of your head.

First hum, then wave your arm, and last raise one foot.

Listening for Details & Main Ideas

Listen carefully. Then answer the question.

There were five candles and a toy train decorating David's birthday cake. It was a delicious chocolate cake with white frosting. What was on top of the birthday cake?

Red is Brittany's favorite color and green is Tyra's favorite color. Darin and Steven like yellow the best. Which color is Brittany's favorite?

Brett was five years old when he learned to tie his shoes. Now he's trying to teach his little sister, Kristi, how to tie her shoes. How old was Brett when he learned to tie his shoes?

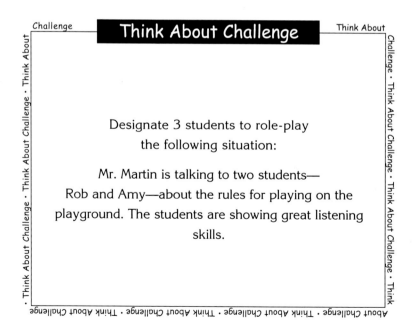

Think About Challenge

Designate 3 students to role-play
the following situation:

Mr. Martin is talking to two students—
Rob and Amy—about the rules for playing on the playground. The students are showing great listening skills.

Listening

Recalling Information

Listen to each set of related words. Then repeat the words in the opposite order that you hear them.

watch, time, clock   *medal, win, prize*

never, always, usually   *cake, cookie, candy*

beach, water, swim   *pizza, pepperoni, crust*

Following Directions

Listen carefully. Then follow the directions.

First show me 2 fingers, then put 4 fingers in the air, and last show me all of your fingers.

First put your hand on your elbow, then put your hand under your shoe, and last put your hand on the chair.

First put your hand on your head, then wave your hand, and last show me your thumb.

First show me your forehead, then point to your nose, and last touch the floor.

First rub your eye, then touch your knee, and last clap your hands 3 times.

Listening for Details & Main Ideas

Listen carefully. Then answer the question.

A dog named Nellie was three years old when she had six puppies. Four of the puppies were girls and two were boys. Nellie and the puppies had golden brown fur and long, floppy ears. Nellie took good care of her puppies until they were eight weeks old. Then all of the puppies went to new homes. Nellie was a good mom to her puppies.

How old was Nellie when she had her puppies?

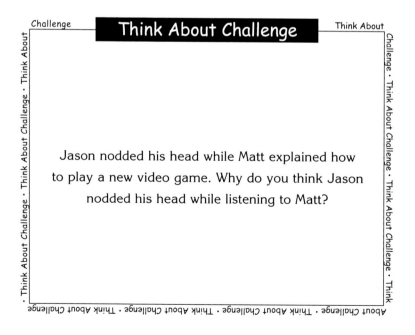

Think About Challenge

Jason nodded his head while Matt explained how to play a new video game. Why do you think Jason nodded his head while listening to Matt?

Listening

Recalling Information

Listen to each set of unrelated words. Then repeat the words in the opposite order that you hear them.

hum, bubble, skip   hoop, look, bake

rose, leap, spaghetti   ladybug, cape, dice

gum, shed, rattle   clue, neat, kite

Following Directions

Listen carefully. Then follow each direction only if Simon says.

Simon says, "First stand up, then turn around, and last clap your hands."

First raise your hand, then touch your feet, and last point to your head.

Simon says, "First touch your eyebrow, then clap your hands, and last point to your nose."

First touch your ears, then point to your knees, and last touch your elbows.

Simon says, "First touch your nose, then point to your feet, and last clap your hands."

Listening for Details & Main Ideas

Listen carefully. Then answer the question.

Marissa and Mark were in the same first-grade class. They also lived next door to each other on Oak Street. On Saturdays, Marissa and Mark often had fun riding bikes together and playing in the neighborhood park. One day, Mark and his family had to move to a new city because Mark's mom got a new job. Now Marissa and Mark write letters to each other.

What street did Marissa and Mark live on?

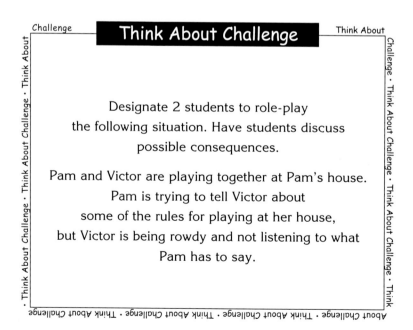

Think About Challenge

Designate 2 students to role-play
the following situation. Have students discuss
possible consequences.

Pam and Victor are playing together at Pam's house.
Pam is trying to tell Victor about
some of the rules for playing at her house,
but Victor is being rowdy and not listening to what
Pam has to say.

Listening

Recalling Information

Listen to each set of unrelated words. Then repeat the words
in the opposite order that you hear them.

slide, apple, hello   cute, snack, dark

tulip, brush, clean   rocket, lid, ripe

tape, never, web   date, bill, lady

Drawing
Activity

Following Directions

Listen carefully. Then follow the directions.

First write your name in the center of the paper, then
draw a box around your name, and last put an *X* at
the bottom of the page.

First draw a circle on the right, then put an *X* in the center
of the circle, and last draw a line under the circle.

First draw a square on the left, then put the number 1 inside
the square, and last put the number 5 below the square.

First draw a pair of lines at the top of the page, then put a
circle to the right of the lines, and last draw a square
to the left of the lines.

First draw a line across the center of the page, then draw
a line down the middle of the page, and last draw a
circle where the 2 lines cross.

Listening for Details & Main Ideas

Listen carefully. Then answer the question.

The city built a new library last May. The old library was too small and couldn't hold all the books, equipment, and people. The new library has 100 new computers and great places to sit and read. The best part about the new library is the outdoor reading area. When the weather is nice, it's fun to sit outside and read a good book. It's not a good idea to sit outside when the weather is rainy, though.

How many new computers are in the new library?

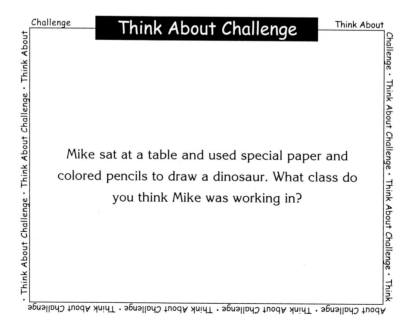

Think About Challenge

Mike sat at a table and used special paper and colored pencils to draw a dinosaur. What class do you think Mike was working in?

Listening

Workout #24

Recalling Information

Listen to each set of numbers. Then repeat the numbers in the opposite order that you hear them.

6, 9, 2, 5

3, 0, 8, 1

7, 4, 9, 2

2, 1, 0, 7

4, 8, 3, 9

5, 7, 2, 6

Following Directions

Drawing Activity

Listen carefully. Then follow the directions.

First draw a square, then put an *X* in the upper right corner of the square, and last write the letter *A* in the bottom left corner of the square.

First draw a square, then write the letter *A* in the right half of the square, and last write the letter *B* in the left half of the square.

First draw a square, then put a line across the center of the square, and last draw a star in the bottom right corner of the square.

First draw a circle, then put a star inside the circle, and last draw a line outside the circle.

First draw a circle, then put a line through the circle, and last draw a flower outside the circle.

76

Listening for Details & Main Ideas

Listen carefully. Then answer the question.

In my opinion, the best bakery in town is Gail's Goodies. They make the most terrific brownies and doughnuts around. They also have the best prices. You can buy 12 doughnuts for just $2. You can also get a whole pan of brownies for just $3. Sometimes we go to the bakery on Saturday mornings to get treats for the weekend. I like to pick out my own goodies.

How much does a pan of brownies cost at Gail's Goodies?

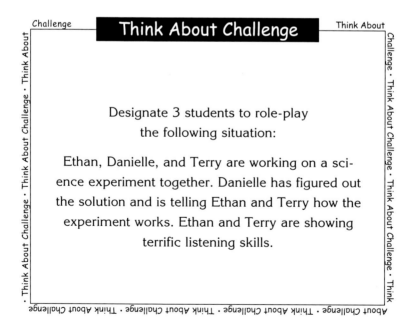

Think About Challenge

Designate 3 students to role-play
the following situation:

Ethan, Danielle, and Terry are working on a science experiment together. Danielle has figured out the solution and is telling Ethan and Terry how the experiment works. Ethan and Terry are showing terrific listening skills.

Listening

Recalling Information

Listen to each set of related words. Then repeat the words in the opposite order that you hear them.

north, south, east, west

egg, fry, bacon, toast

duck, hen, rooster, goose

add, subtract, multiply, divide

brother, sister, mother, father

Following Directions

Listen carefully. Then follow each direction only if Simon says.

Simon says, "First raise your left arm in the air, then clap your hands, and last wave your hand."

First stand up, then say your name, and last turn around.

Simon says, "First count to 3, then clap your hands twice, and last say your name."

Simon says, "First hold up 2 fingers, then wave your hand, and last rub your head."

First count to 5, then touch your knee, and last touch your ear.

Listening for Details & Main Ideas

Listen carefully. Then answer the question.

I was starting to think that my little sister was taking money from my piggy bank, so I hid it in the back of my closet. Later I found out that she was not taking my money. I think I'll still keep it hidden so that I don't get tempted to take money myself. I just hope I don't forget where I hid it. Maybe I'll write myself a note so I won't forget.

Where did I hide my piggy bank?

Think About Challenge

Why might it be difficult to listen when you are really hungry?

Listening

Recalling Information

Listen to each set of related words. Then repeat the words in the opposite order that you hear them.

thread, needle, sew, yarn

bracelet, earring, ring, necklace

Jack, Queen, King, ace

umbrella, rain, wet, puddle

hungry, eat, stomach, growl

Following Directions

Listen carefully. Then follow the directions.

First touch your left knee, then touch your right ear, and last touch your left eye.

First touch your right foot, then touch your left arm, and last touch your right elbow.

First touch your forehead, then touch your right shoulder, and last touch your left ear.

First touch your eye, then bend over, and last say your name.

First touch your left eyebrow, then touch your right knee, and last touch your nose.

Listening for Details & Main Ideas

Listen carefully. Then answer the question.

Our class trip was cancelled because of bad weather. We were supposed to go to the park for the day to celebrate the end of the school year. We were going to roast hot dogs, play volleyball, and throw the Frisbee around. It started to storm last night and the park was flooded this morning. Instead of going to the park, we had an indoor picnic in our classroom. We didn't roast hot dogs, but we ate bologna sandwiches.

What games were we going to play at the park?

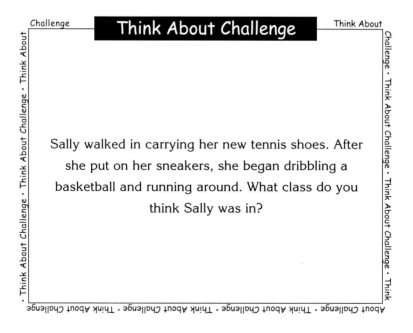

Challenge · Think About

Think About Challenge

Think About

Sally walked in carrying her new tennis shoes. After she put on her sneakers, she began dribbling a basketball and running around. What class do you think Sally was in?

Listening

Recalling Information

Listen to each set of unrelated words. Then repeat the words in the opposite order that you hear them.

China, hike, friend, toe

shark, cone, rhyme, beak

tooth, dimple, top, sink

desert, tax, seed, bus

plus, told, game, sale

Following Directions

Listen carefully. Then follow the directions.

First raise your left foot, then raise your right arm, and last raise your eyebrows.

First wave your left arm, then touch your right knee, and last raise your left leg.

First touch your right shoulder, then touch your left eye, and last touch your head.

First touch the bottom of your foot, then touch the top of your head, and last touch your left elbow.

First hold up 3 fingers, then blink your eyes, and last touch your foot.

Listening for Details & Main Ideas

Listen carefully. Then answer the question.

My parents just bought a new van that can hold nine people. Our old car was starting to make strange noises, so they really thought it was time to get a new vehicle. Our new van is blue and has a sparkly stripe down the side. It is a great looking van and we have fun riding in it. It can hold my parents, my grandparents, my brother, my sister, and me. And there's still room left!

How many people can fit in the new van?

Think About Challenge

Tell 3 things that might make it hard for you to be a good listener.

Listening

Recalling Information

Listen to each set of unrelated words. Then repeat the words in the opposite order that you hear them.

van, fence, brick, key

beard, vine, right, voice

party, core, lump, sap

radio, sick, brownie, hip

butter, story, reach, trim

Following Directions

Listen carefully. Then follow the directions.

First count to 5, then hold up 4 fingers, and last say your name.

First clap your hands, then touch the bottom of your foot, and last touch the top of your head.

First touch your shoes, then clap your hands, and last kick your left foot in the air.

First touch the bottom of your nose, then touch the side of your nose, and last touch the top of your nose.

First raise your hand, then clap your hands, and last stomp your foot.

Listening for Details & Main Ideas

Listen carefully. Then answer the question.

The principal, Mrs. Craig, just won a big award. Because she is a terrific principal, she gets to go to Washington, DC, to receive a special plaque and certificate. She might even get a chance to meet the President of the United States. Mrs. Craig always takes time to stop and talk to students in the hallway, and she comes to our class sometimes, too, to watch a lesson. We are all so happy that she is getting this award.

Who is receiving a special award?

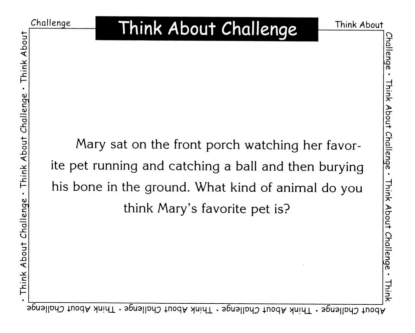

Think About Challenge

Mary sat on the front porch watching her favorite pet running and catching a ball and then burying his bone in the ground. What kind of animal do you think Mary's favorite pet is?

Listening

Workout #29

Recalling Information

Listen to each set of related words. Then repeat the words in the opposite order that you hear them.

in, out, up, down, around

tree, nest, bird, egg, fly

store, buy, price, money, pay

dog, bark, collar, flea, leash

peas, beans, corn, carrots, onions

Following Directions

Listen carefully. Then follow the directions.

First put your hand on your head, then put your hand near your head, and last put your hand far from your head.

First put your hand in the center of your head, then put 1 foot ahead of the other foot, and last put your hand to the right of your head.

First put your hand in the middle of your forehead, then put your hand on the right side of your face, and last put your finger on the left side of your face.

First raise your hand, then touch your first finger, and last touch your thumb.

Listening for Details & Main Ideas

Listen carefully. Then answer the question.

June is the busiest month of the year in my parents' store. The store sells camping supplies and hiking equipment. Everything you would need to take a camping trip or go hiking is for sale in their store. I like to walk up and down the aisles and check out all the neat supplies. Some of the tents are so big that my whole family could fit inside one. We take camping trips all summer long.

Which month of the year is the busiest at my parents' store?

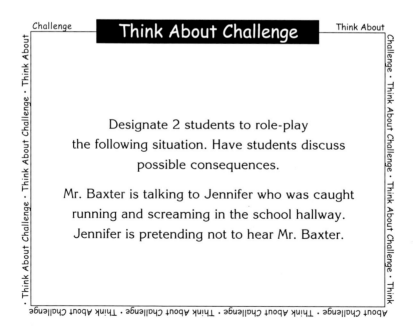

Think About Challenge

Designate 2 students to role-play the following situation. Have students discuss possible consequences.

Mr. Baxter is talking to Jennifer who was caught running and screaming in the school hallway. Jennifer is pretending not to hear Mr. Baxter.

Listening

Recalling Information

Listen to each set of unrelated words. Then repeat the words in the opposite order that you hear them.

rug, mitt, wide, cow, well

banjo, seat, go, lap, news

fin, tent, pal, shelf, litter

silver, far, bag, phone, wink

jet, vase, fence, wind, germ

Following Directions

Listen carefully. Then follow each direction only if Simon says.

First stand up, then turn around, and last clap your hands.

Simon says, "First wave your right hand, then stand up, and last raise your left foot."

First touch your left elbow, then shake your right foot, and last touch your left eye.

Simon says, "First raise your right arm, then touch your left shoulder, and last kick your right foot in the air."

Simon says, "First clap your hands, then kick your right foot in the air, and last shake your head up and down."

Listening for Details & Main Ideas

Listen carefully. Then answer the question.

Camilla and Craig both have their birthdays on August 16. Camilla will be 10 years old on her next birthday, but Craig will only be turning 5. Camilla and Craig are also sister and brother. Sometimes they like having the same birthday because it becomes a really big party. Sometimes they wish they had separate days to celebrate. One year, Camilla and Craig did celebrate their birthdays on different days.

How old will Craig be on his next birthday?

Think About Challenge

Why might it be difficult to listen well
when someone is speaking very quietly?

 # Listening

Workout #31

Recalling Information

Listen to each nonsense word. Then repeat it.

grive   krackmoq

nangeez   ploitso

brogfan   grafrob

Following Directions

Listen carefully. Then follow the directions.

First put 1 penny in the upper right corner of the paper, then put 2 pennies in the lower left corner of the paper, and last put 3 pennies in the lower right corner of the paper.

First draw a circle on the paper, then put 3 pennies inside the circle, and last put 4 pennies outside the circle.

First draw a long line across the center of the paper, then put 2 pennies above the line, and last put 3 pennies below the line.

First draw a short line down the middle of the paper, then put 2 pennies at each end of the line, and last put 1 penny on the right side of the line.

First draw a square, then put 1 penny in the center of the square, and last write your name at the bottom of the paper.

Listening for Details & Main Ideas

Listen to the following information. Then tell the main idea.

> Juice can be a healthy drink but children should not drink too much of it. Juice contains a lot of sugar. Even though sugary juice tastes good, it can be bad for a child's teeth. Children should drink juice that has 100% fruit juice. Also, they should drink only one or two glasses per day.

> What is the main idea of the information you just heard?

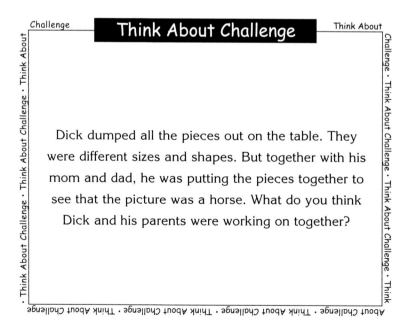

Think About Challenge

Dick dumped all the pieces out on the table. They were different sizes and shapes. But together with his mom and dad, he was putting the pieces together to see that the picture was a horse. What do you think Dick and his parents were working on together?

Listening

Workout #32

Recalling Information

Listen to each nonsense word. Then repeat it.

yipbo   krig

chazoil   brogfen

reeweez   flaplo

Following Directions

Listen carefully. Then follow the directions.

First show me angry, then show me worried, and last show me bored.

First show me upset, then show me guilty, and last show me shy.

First show me confident, then show me ashamed, and last show me nervous.

First show me jealous, then show me proud, and last show me embarrassed.

First show me frightened, then show me hopeful, and last show me ecstatic.

Listening for Details & Main Ideas

Listen to the following information. Then tell the main idea.

It is very important to wear a bicycle helmet whenever you ride a bike. People can get hurt very badly if they fall off of a bike and hit their head while not wearing a helmet. Helmets come in all sorts of styles and colors. You can buy bike helmets at bike shops and department stores. It is also important to find out how to wear a helmet the right way. The people at the police station or fire department can show you how to wear a helmet properly.

What is the main idea of the information you just heard?

Think About Challenge

Designate 2 students to role-play
the following situation:

Daven and Shannon are talking on the telephone.
They are telling each other about what they did over
the weekend. Both children are showing great
listening skills.

Listening

Workout #33

Recalling Information

Listen to each nonsense word. Then repeat it.

grobile   jokral

jorteed   vesgra

trycrowl   dentog

Drawing Activity

Following Directions

Listen carefully. Then follow the directions.

First draw a rectangle, then put a star in the upper right corner of the rectangle, and last put a tree in the lower left corner of the rectangle.

First draw a square with a star in the middle, then draw a short line above the square, and last draw a circle to the left of the square.

First draw a tree, then put a star at the top of the tree, and last draw a circle under the tree.

First draw 2 circles, then draw a line connecting the circles, and last write your name under the circles.

First draw a long line, then put a star to the right of the line, and last draw a flower to left of the line.

Listening for Details & Main Ideas

Listen to the following information. Then tell the main idea.

Eating fruits and vegetables every day is important to stay healthy and strong. Most doctors say that it is good to get five or six servings of fruits and vegetables each day. Fruits and vegetables can be eaten fresh or cooked. There are many different recipes that can be used to prepare fruits and vegetables. Fruits and vegetables are usually very affordable.

What is the main idea of the information you just heard?

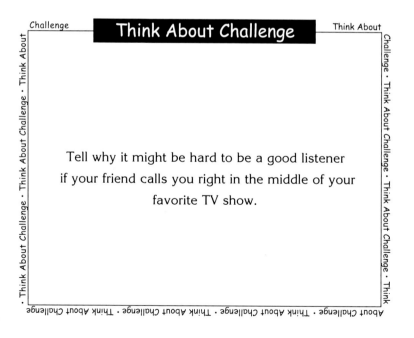

Think About Challenge

Tell why it might be hard to be a good listener if your friend calls you right in the middle of your favorite TV show.

 # Listening

Recalling Information

Listen to each nonsense word. Then repeat it.

nalleer	*pirg*
zeenoy	*stugray*
grung	*detule*

Following Directions

Listen carefully. Then follow the directions.

First clap your hands, then stand up, then turn around, and last wave your hand.

First say your name, then clap your hands, then show me 3 fingers, and last count to 5.

First wave your hand, then count to 3, then show me your thumb, and last say your name.

First stomp your foot, then touch your knee, then touch your stomach, and last touch your head.

First wave good-bye, then touch your right thumb, then touch your hair, and last touch your nose.

Listening for Details & Main Ideas

Listen to the following information. Then tell the main idea.

> Computers have many important and fun uses. Companies use computers every day to help run their businesses. Schools use computers to help students learn. The government uses computers to keep track of information and paperwork. Computers are also great to use to play games. There are computer games for people of all ages. Even adults like to use computers to play games. Many people use computers to surf the Web and to send and receive email.

What is the main idea of the information you just heard?

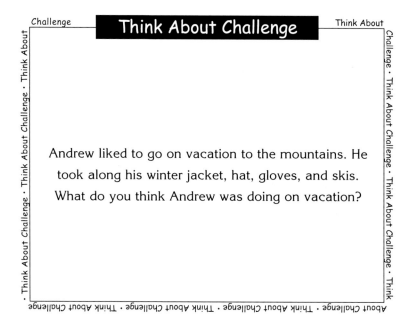

Think About Challenge

Andrew liked to go on vacation to the mountains. He took along his winter jacket, hat, gloves, and skis. What do you think Andrew was doing on vacation?

 # Listening

Recalling Information

Listen to each nonsense word. Then repeat it.

twum   *hithwoo*

kwamstil   *nellav*

brepsew   *wermut*

Following Directions

Listen carefully. Then follow the directions.

First clap your hands, then touch your foot, then touch your ears, and last say your name.

First spell your name, then count to 5, then stomp your foot, and last touch your hair.

First touch your knee, then touch your right elbow, then clap your hands, and last touch your ears.

First raise your hands, then touch your foot, then spell *cat,* and last touch your head.

First wave your hand, then touch your elbow, then spell *dog,* and last say your name.

Listening for Details & Main Ideas

Listen to the following information. Then tell the main idea.

Children should not watch too much TV. There are many programs on TV that children should not watch. There are usually better things for children to do, like playing outside, reading, working on the computer, and playing board games with family and friends. Some TV programs are OK for children to watch, but watching TV should never be the most important part of a child's day. Some of the safer TV shows to watch are usually on right before and after the school day.

What is the main idea of the information you just heard?

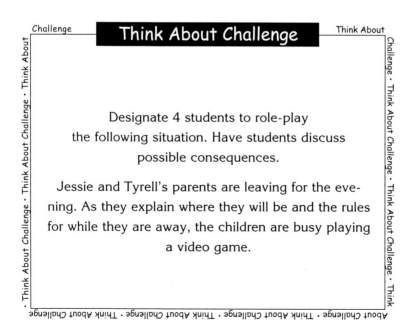

Think About Challenge

Designate 4 students to role-play
the following situation. Have students discuss
possible consequences.

Jessie and Tyrell's parents are leaving for the evening. As they explain where they will be and the rules for while they are away, the children are busy playing a video game.

# Listening

Recalling Information

Listen to each nonsense word. Then repeat it.

filampito   *teewoza*

zonandola   *lipogellar*

yobeegato   *bodoka*

Following Directions

Listen carefully. Then follow the directions.

First raise your hand, then touch your elbow, then touch your knee, and last hold up 4 fingers.

First blink your eyes, then touch your head, then say your name, and last jump 1 time.

First touch your shoulder, then wave your hand, then touch the bottom of your shoe, and last touch the top of your head.

First stand up, then turn around, then jump up 1 time, and last count to 3.

First touch the center of your head, then touch the bottom of your nose, then touch the side of your head, and last touch the top of your head.

Listening for Details & Main Ideas

Listen to the following information. Then tell the main idea.

Sports are a great way for children to stay strong and healthy. Some sports, like basketball and soccer, are played as a team. Other sports, like swimming and tennis, can be played without a team. It is good to play both team sports and individual sports. Some sports, like golf, can be expensive to play, but sports like running don't cost any money at all. Children can try lots of different sports to find out what they are best at and what they have the most fun doing.

What is the main idea of the information you just heard?

Think About Challenge

Why is it a good idea for you to face someone who is talking to you?

Listening

Recalling Information

Listen to each nonsense word. Then repeat it.

britakski   gretaybesho

lenisore   frambeewo

zreksala   neshellowa

Following Directions

Listen carefully. Then follow the directions.

First say your name, then clap your hands, then stomp your feet, and last touch your elbow.

First wave your hand, then kick your foot, then touch your hair, and last blink your eyes.

First hold up 2 fingers, then touch your right thumb, then touch your left knee, and last touch your right elbow.

First hold up 3 fingers, then touch your left ear, then touch your right ear, and last touch the top of your head.

First wave good-bye, then show me your thumb, then touch your head, and last touch your stomach.

Listening for Details & Main Ideas

Listen to the following information. Then tell the main idea.

Working for an allowance is a great way to earn money. An allowance is the money you earn when you do chores around the house. Some kids need to make their bed, keep their room clean, and help with other chores around the house in order to earn their allowance. You can save part of your allowance and then spend some of it on fun things like going to a movie or buying a new CD.

What is the main idea of the information you just heard?

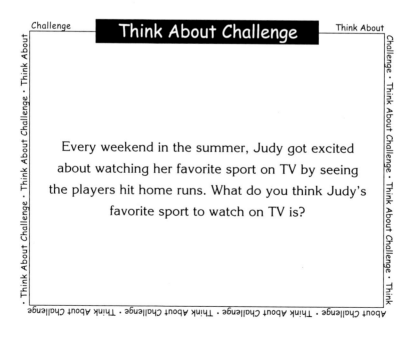

Think About Challenge

Every weekend in the summer, Judy got excited about watching her favorite sport on TV by seeing the players hit home runs. What do you think Judy's favorite sport to watch on TV is?

 # Listening

Recalling Information

Listen to each nonsense word. Then repeat it.

sabroola   tintwokila

chiwooku   gimcogo

neelaygan   yortencina

Following Directions

Listen carefully. Then follow the directions.

First draw a circle on the left side of the paper, then put 2 pennies inside the circle, then put 1 penny in the lower right corner of the paper, and last write your name in the upper right corner of the paper.

First put 2 pennies in the center of the paper, then put 1 penny in each corner of the paper, then put 1 penny on the bottom of the paper, and last put 3 pennies outside the paper.

First draw a circle, then put 3 pennies in the center of the circle, then put 2 pennies outside the circle, and last write your name in the lower left corner of the paper.

First put 1 penny in the lower left corner of the paper, then put 1 penny in the upper right corner of the paper, then put 1 penny in the middle of the paper, and last put 1 penny in the upper left corner of the paper.

Listening for Details & Main Ideas

Listen to the following information. Then tell the main idea.

Having good hygiene means keeping yourself and your things clean. It's important to be clean every day. Taking a bath or shower whenever needed, brushing your hair and teeth every day, and wearing clean clothes are all parts of having good hygiene. It is also important to wash your hands every time you use the restroom. Soaps, toothpaste, and detergents are all useful for keeping people and clothing clean.

What is the main idea of the information you just heard?

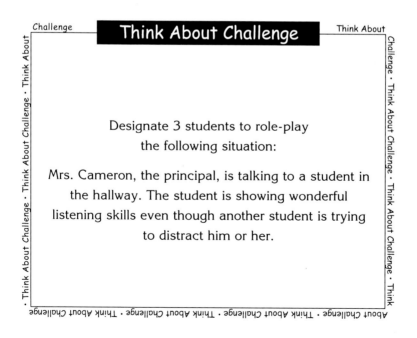

Think About Challenge

Designate 3 students to role-play
the following situation:

Mrs. Cameron, the principal, is talking to a student in the hallway. The student is showing wonderful listening skills even though another student is trying to distract him or her.

Listening

Workout #39

Recalling Information

Listen to each nonsense word. Then repeat it.

bowlidma   swidnalogo

pazhindi   mohoozbra

bratinger   yustotoma

Following Directions

Listen carefully. Then follow the directions.

First show me sad, then show me happy, then show me afraid, and last show me worried.

First show me happy, then show me tired, then show me funny, and last show me bored.

First show me confused, then show me bored, then show me worried, and last show me happy.

First show me excited, then show me crying, then show me happy, and last show me surprised.

First show me sad, then show me angry, then show me happy, and last show me bored.

Listening for Details & Main Ideas

Listen to the following information. Then tell the main idea.

Owning a pet is a big responsibility. Pets need a lot of care. They need to be fed, kept clean, and played with. Some pets need to be exercised too. Pets like dogs and cats need a lot more attention than pets like fish and birds. Pets can also be expensive. Dogs and horses cost more to care for than fish and hamsters. All pets should be treated with love.

What is the main idea of the information you just heard?

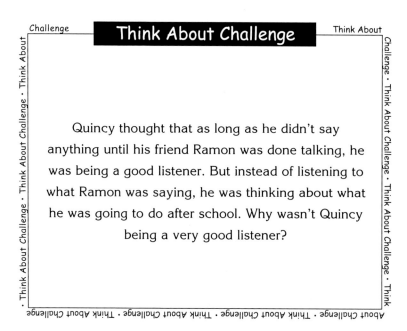

Think About Challenge

Quincy thought that as long as he didn't say anything until his friend Ramon was done talking, he was being a good listener. But instead of listening to what Ramon was saying, he was thinking about what he was going to do after school. Why wasn't Quincy being a very good listener?

Listening

Workout #40

Recalling Information

Listen to each nonsense word. Then repeat it.

afrowlsty   pidranky

tainobula   mulabango

shedderlig   famcilapo

Following Directions

Listen carefully. Then follow the directions.

First put your hand on top of your head, then put your hand beside your head, then put your hand on the left side of your head, and last put your hand away from your head.

First put your hand in the center of your head, then jump up once, then put 1 foot ahead of the other foot, and last put your hand to the right of your head.

First put your hand in the middle of your forehead, then put your hand on the right side of your face, then touch your right shoulder, and last put your finger on the left side of your face.

First raise your hand, then touch your head, then touch your first finger, and last touch your thumb.

Listening for Details & Main Ideas

Listen to the following information. Then tell the main idea.

Bats can be very helpful animals. Bats are small, flying creatures that can be found in many places in the world. Some people are afraid of bats because think they are dangerous. But bats are not very dangerous. They help the environment because they eat insects. If bats did not exist, the insect population would get out of control. We would have insects everywhere and we wouldn't be able to be outside much.

What is the main idea of the information you just heard?

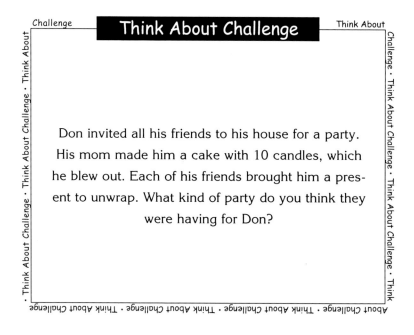

Think About Challenge

Don invited all his friends to his house for a party. His mom made him a cake with 10 candles, which he blew out. Each of his friends brought him a present to unwrap. What kind of party do you think they were having for Don?

Listening

Recalling Information

Listen to each sentence. Then repeat it.

Her sister plays with dolls.

The books are in your backpack.

Heather shuffled the cards really well.

Our dog ran through the neighbor's yard.

Yesterday I wrote a letter to my grandpa.

Following Directions Drawing Activity

Listen carefully. Then follow the directions.

First draw a rectangle, then put a star in the upper right corner and a circle in the lower right corner of the rectangle, and last put a heart in the upper left corner and a triangle in the lower left corner of the rectangle.

First draw a square with a star in the middle, then draw a line to the right of the star, then draw a flower to the right of the line, and last draw a circle to the left of the line.

First draw a tree with a star at the top, then put a circle on the left side of the tree, then put a square on the right side of the tree, and last put a circle under the tree.

First draw a circle, then draw a square on the right side of the circle, then draw a star on the left side of the circle, and last put a circle around the star.

110

Listening for Details & Main Ideas

Listen to the following information. Then answer the question.

On Friday evening, the Howard family decided to go out for pizza and to a movie. They stopped at the movie theatre first to buy their tickets and then headed to the pizza place. After eating, they got in their car to drive to the movie. What a bummer! Their car wouldn't start. The movie was going to start in 10 minutes, but they couldn't get their car started.

What do you think the Howard family might do next?

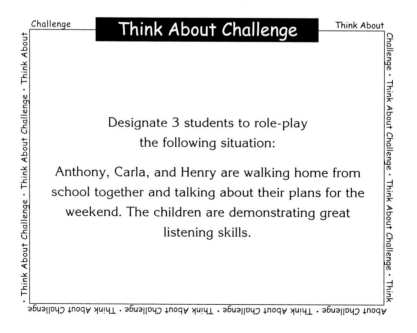

Think About Challenge

Designate 3 students to role-play
the following situation:

Anthony, Carla, and Henry are walking home from school together and talking about their plans for the weekend. The children are demonstrating great listening skills.

Listening

Recalling Information

Listen to each sentence. Then repeat it.

The blue car was blocking the driveway.

The horses were covered in mud.

Sam is not coming to my birthday party.

Exercise is important to keep you healthy.

She would like to go for a walk around the lake today.

Following Directions

Listen carefully. Then follow the directions.

First clap your hands, then touch your foot, then touch your eyes, then touch your ears, and last say your name.

First spell your name, then count to 4, then touch your ear, then stomp your foot, and last touch your hair.

First touch your knee, then touch your right elbow, then jump up once, then clap your hands, and last touch your ears.

First raise your hands, then touch your foot, then wave good-bye, then spell *chair*, and last touch your head.

Listening for Details & Main Ideas

Listen to the following information. Then answer the question.

Michael was riding his bike to school when he saw an ambulance racing down the street. He stopped to let the ambulance pass by and then he watched it continue down the street. He looked at his watch and noticed that the school bell was going to ring any minute now. He took one last peek back at the ambulance and noticed it turn down his street. Michael knew that his parents and grandmother were at his house and he wondered if someone there was hurt or sick.

What do you think Michael did next?

Think About Challenge

Why might you have a hard time listening when you don't feel well?

Listening

Recalling Information

Listen to each sentence. Then repeat it.

The days are hot, but the nights are cold.

Last winter, I fell on the ice and I broke my arm.

He shared his games with me, but you don't have to.

Sam is going to Grandma's today or else he's staying home.

I'm taking piano lessons and I'm going to camp this year.

Following Directions

Listen carefully. Then follow each direction only if Simon says.

First say your name, then clap your hands, then stand up, then turn around, and last wave your hand.

First stand up, then say your name, then clap your hands, then show me 3 fingers, and last count to 5.

Simon says, "First wave your hand, then count to 3, then show me your thumb, then spell *happy*, and last say your name."

Simon says, "First stomp your foot, then touch your knee, then touch your stomach, then touch the top of your head, and last touch your nose."

Listening for Details & Main Ideas

Listen to the following information. Then answer the question.

> Our family purchased a new computer last weekend. At first, we were very excited to set it up and start using it to play games. After about two days of trying, my parents and older brother still couldn't get the computer working right. Now a week has passed and I still haven't gotten to play any of my new games.
>
> What do you think my parents will do now?

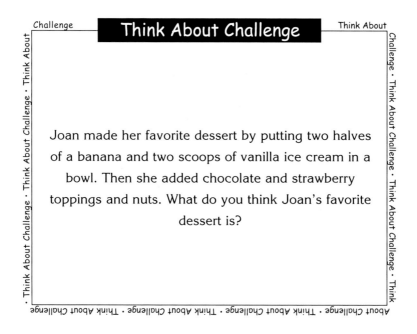

Think About Challenge

Joan made her favorite dessert by putting two halves of a banana and two scoops of vanilla ice cream in a bowl. Then she added chocolate and strawberry toppings and nuts. What do you think Joan's favorite dessert is?

Listening

Recalling Information

Listen to each sentence. Then repeat it.

When you leave the room, please turn out the lights.

If you want to come with us, just say so.

Alison sat on the bench while the other kids played.

Because my brother is 16, he can drive a car.

You should wear a blue shirt, unless you don't want to.

Following Directions

Listen carefully. Then follow each direction only if Simon says.

Simon says, "First clap your hands, then wave your hand, then touch your nose, then touch your left ear, and last turn around."

Simon says, "First blink your eyes, then touch your forehead, then show me your right hand, then touch your hair, and last touch your foot."

First touch your elbow, then hold up 2 fingers, then touch your thumb, then say your name, and last count to 3.

First turn around, then jump up 1 time, then touch your shoulder, then bend over, and last touch your toes.

Listening for Details & Main Ideas

Listen to the following information. Then answer the question.

> Elizabeth and Jackson were best friends. They grew up next door to each other and played together almost every day during summer vacations. Just last month, Elizabeth's parents told her that they had to move. Elizabeth's family would be living in a new city far away from Jackson.

> How do you think Elizabeth might feel?

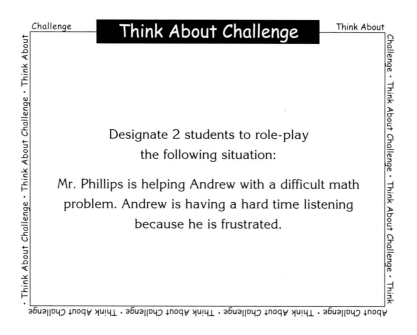

Think About Challenge

Designate 2 students to role-play
the following situation:

Mr. Phillips is helping Andrew with a difficult math problem. Andrew is having a hard time listening because he is frustrated.

Listening

Recalling Information

Listen to each question. Then repeat it.

Is tomorrow Friday or Saturday?

Will you go to the store with me at 2:00?

Can you do 100 push-ups in a row?

Are the pencils in the desk drawer sharpened yet?

Do all little, brown dogs have fleas?

Following Directions

Listen carefully. Then follow the directions.

First show me sad, then show me happy, then show me angry, then show me afraid, and last show me surprised.

First show me tired, then show me excited, then show me afraid, then show me bored, and last show me happy.

First show me happy, then show me sad, then show me bored, then show me scared, and last show me worried.

First show me tired, then show me worried, then show me happy, then show me confused, and last show me afraid.

Listening for Details & Main Ideas

Listen to the following information. Then answer the question.

> On her way to school, Samantha lost her lunch money. She checked in all of her pockets and in her backpack, but she couldn't find it anywhere. She asked her best friends if she could borrow some money, but they didn't have any either. They brought their lunches from home.

> What do you think Samantha might do to solve her problem?

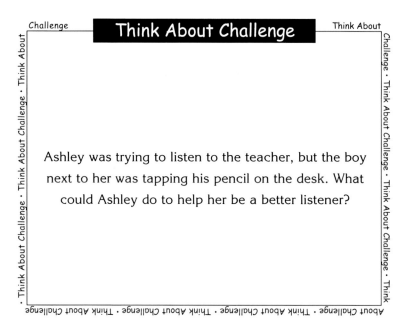

Think About Challenge

Ashley was trying to listen to the teacher, but the boy next to her was tapping his pencil on the desk. What could Ashley do to help her be a better listener?

Listening

Recalling Information

Listen to each question. Then repeat it.

Weren't they supposed to go to Florida this summer?

Aren't you going to share your pizza with me?

Doesn't her mom already have two brand-new cars?

Isn't that the girl we saw at the mall yesterday?

Can't I clean my room tomorrow so I can go play now?

Following Directions

Listen carefully. Then follow the directions.

First clap your hands, then stand up, then turn around, then jump up once, and last wave your hand.

First say your name, then clap your hands, then wave your hand, then show me 3 fingers, and last count to 5.

First show me 3 fingers, then wave your hand, then count to 3, then show me your thumb, and last say your name.

First stomp your foot, then touch your knee, then touch your stomach, then touch your ear, and last touch your head.

120

Listening for Details & Main Ideas

Listen to the following information. Then answer the question.

Curtis checked out two books and one computer game from the public library. He read only one of the books and only played the game a couple of times before the due date came along. Curtis really wants to read the other book and wants to have more time to play the game, but he knows the items are due back at the library.

What do you think Curtis could do?

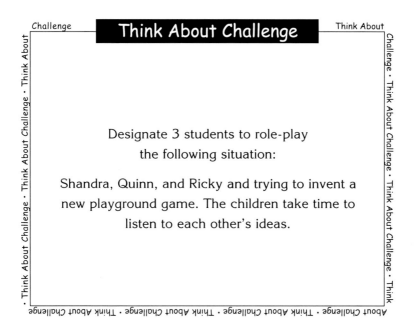

Challenge • Think About

Think About Challenge

Think About

Designate 3 students to role-play
the following situation:

Shandra, Quinn, and Ricky and trying to invent a
new playground game. The children take time to
listen to each other's ideas.

Listening

Recalling Information

Listen to each question. Then repeat it.

Who helps you with your homework?

What color is the sky today?

Where do you keep your extra pens?

Who is your favorite singer right now?

What is the boy in the green shirt doing?

Following Directions

Listen carefully. Then follow the directions.

First put 2 pennies in the center of the paper, then put 3 pennies on the left side of the paper, then put 1 penny on the bottom of the paper, then put 1 penny on the top of the paper, and last put 3 pennies outside the paper.

First put 7 pennies in a row and draw a circle around the pennies, then put 1 penny in each left corner of the paper, and last write your name above the circle.

First draw a square in the middle of the paper, then put 4 pennies inside the square, then place 2 pennies above the square and 3 pennies to the right of the square, and last draw a line down the left side of the paper.

122

Listening for Details & Main Ideas

Listen to the following information. Then answer the question.

Ben and Jamie wanted to make a special anniversary breakfast for their parents. The kids got up extra early and started to make toast, cereal, and juice without making too much noise. They didn't want their parents to hear, because they wanted the breakfast-in-bed to be a surprise. While they were making the toast, the toaster started smoking.

What might Ben and Jamie do now?

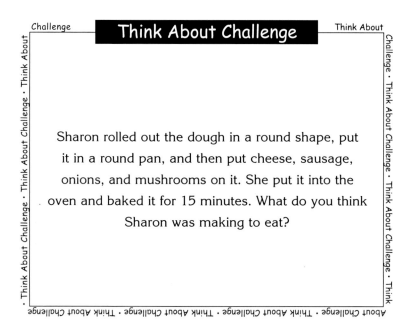

Think About Challenge

Sharon rolled out the dough in a round shape, put it in a round pan, and then put cheese, sausage, onions, and mushrooms on it. She put it into the oven and baked it for 15 minutes. What do you think Sharon was making to eat?

Listening

Workout #48

Recalling Information

Listen to each question. Then repeat it.

Why do people wear mittens when it snows?

How do you feel if you stay up too late?

When do you go to bed each night?

Where is your favorite hiding place?

Which flavor do you like better: chocolate or vanilla?

Following Directions

Listen carefully. Then follow each direction only if Simon says.

Simon says, "First raise your hand, then touch your elbow, then touch your shoulder, then touch your knee, and last hold up 4 fingers."

First count to 5, then blink your eyes, then touch your head, then say your name, and last jump 1 time.

Simon says, "First touch your shoulder, then spell *sad*, then wave your hand, then touch the bottom of your shoe, and last touch the top of your head."

Simon says, "First stand up, then turn around, then jump up 1 time, then wave good-bye, and last count to 3."

124

Listening for Details & Main Ideas

Listen to the following information. Then answer the question.

Jaden and Brooke were best friends. They were in the same third-grade class at school and were always kind to each other. One day, Jaden thought she saw Brooke take something from the teacher's purse. Jaden didn't know what to do.

What might Jaden do about what she thought she saw?

Challenge — **Think About Challenge** — Think About

Tell why it might be hard to draw a picture and listen to someone talk to you at the same time.

125

Listening

Workout #49

Recalling Information

Listen to each sentence. Then repeat it.

If it snows, we'll go shopping and I'll get some new boots.

I lost my key, so I couldn't get in until my mom came home.

He tries to do it all by himself, but when he does, he gets confused.

If his mom agrees, we can pick up Jo and you two can play.

Since she left, I've gotten a lot more work done and I feel great.

Following Directions

Drawing Activity

Listen carefully. Then follow the directions.

First draw a rectangle, then put a star in the upper right corner and a tree in the lower left corner, and last draw a circle and put a star in the middle of the circle.

First draw a square with a star in the middle, then draw a line to the right of the star, then draw a circle to the left of the star, then draw a square in the middle of the circle, and last put and X inside the square.

First draw a tree, then put a star at the top of the tree, then put 2 circles on the left side of the tree, then put 3 circles on the right side of the tree, and last put a circle under the tree.

126

Listening for Details & Main Ideas

Listen to the following information. Then answer the question.

There were six slices of bread left in the kitchen when Francis went to bed one night. The next morning when she was making her lunch for school, there was no bread to be found. Her parents were already gone for the day, and Francis needed to take a lunch to school.

What do you think Francis could do?

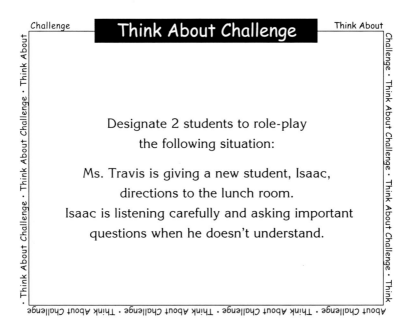

Think About Challenge

Designate 2 students to role-play the following situation:

Ms. Travis is giving a new student, Isaac, directions to the lunch room.
Isaac is listening carefully and asking important questions when he doesn't understand.

Listening

Recalling Information

Listen to each question. Then repeat it.

Do you want to eat now or should we wait until Dad gets home?

Have you been waiting in line or did you just get here?

I don't like grape bubble gum, do you?

Goldfish can't swim upside-down, can they?

There are no other kids at this party, are there?

Following Directions

Listen carefully. Then follow the directions.

First put your hand on top of your head, then beside your head, then on the left side of your head, then behind your head, and last away from your head.

First put your hand in front of your head, then jump up once, then put 1 foot ahead of the other foot, then count to 5, and last sit down.

First put your hand on of your forehead, then on the right side of your face, then on your right shoulder, then on your right knee, and last on the left side of your face.

Listening for Details & Main Ideas

Listen to the following information. Then answer the question.

It was a cold and stormy day. Julia and Jeffrey decided to play inside since the weather was so awful. Toward the middle of the day, Julia let their dog, Pepper, outside to go to the bathroom. A few minutes later, when Julia went to bring Pepper inside, she realized Pepper was gone and the fence gate was wide open. Julia called for Jeffrey.

What do you think might happen next?

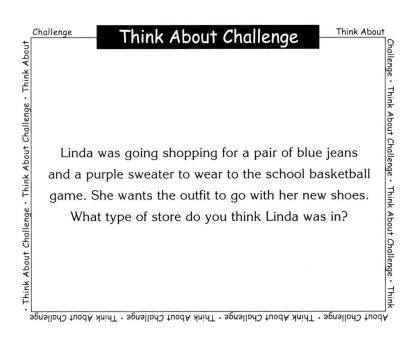

Think About Challenge

Linda was going shopping for a pair of blue jeans and a purple sweater to wear to the school basketball game. She wants the outfit to go with her new shoes. What type of store do you think Linda was in?